Peak
District

Paul Gannon

 Pesda Press LTD

www.pesdapress.com

Cover photo: Hen Cloud viewed from the Roaches.

First published in Great Britain 2010 by Pesda Press
Unit 22, Galeri
Doc Victoria
Caernarfon
Gwynedd
LL55 1SQ

© Copyright 2010 Paul Gannon
All photographs by Paul Gannon

ISBN: 978-1-906095-24-6

Printed and bound in China.

Grit and peat on Kinder Scout.

Contents

Introduction

The Peak District is England's most popular hill-walking area. Its varied scenery has attracted praise from writers and naturalists as well as those who seek out the pleasures of natural beauty and outdoor exercise. For more than three centuries its mix of intriguing dale and invigorating hills, easy walking on grassy fields and tough going on moorlands of bog and its unusual limestone scenery with dry valleys, deep gorges and underground drainage systems have captured the imagination and aroused the desire to get out in the fresh air.

Many of those who walk through this marvellous landscape, teasingly placed between major conurbations, wonder why it looks like it does. What created the immense variety of landscape in the Peak District? What is the role of the underlying geology and what is the contribution of human beings? Why is the White Peak so grassy, scattered with dry valleys,

Photo 0.1
White Peak scenery
– Chrome Hill seen
from Parkhouse
Hill, Dove valley.

gorges, sink holes, fossil sites and the remains of mine workings as well as modern day quarries and cement works? Why is the Dark Peak so different, with its rolling moorland, endless acres of bog, heather and rocky 'edges'?

This book attempts to help walkers and other visitors to answer such questions. This book is in two parts. The first seven chapters record the fascinating story of how colliding continents, violent volcanoes, irresistible mountain-building forces combined with millions and millions of years of slow accumulation of 'sedimentary' rocks such as 'limestone', 'grit', 'sandstone' and 'shale', as well as fierce erosion by glaciation have shaped the landscape we see nowadays. I attempt to explain what sort of rocks were created and how to recognise signs of immensely violent 'tectonic' forces, to spot evidence of tropical seas full of life, and to look for indications of glaciation on the hills and in the dales today. The second part of the book contains 15 recommended walks, with a wide variety of geological features and consistently excellent views of the best of the Peak District's wonderful scenery.

I hope the reader will derive more pleasure from walking the fells through appreciating something of the combined influence of volcanoes, glaciation, erosion and the like on the present-day landscape. The book concentrates on what you can see as you walk about, without recourse to a hand lens or other specialist geologists' tools. The aim is to enable the reader to identify major and minor landscape features in the Peak District and maybe

Photo 0.2 | Dark Peak scenery – viewing the landscape from Kinder Scout's southern edge.

elsewhere too. The landscape we see before us is the product of many different forces and factors. Identifying and unravelling these different forces and factors on the ground is an endlessly fascinating pastime for the landscape lover.

Photo 0.3

Kinder Low.

This book is written specifically with the walker in mind. While geology is a fascinating subject it is also a science; it relies on a complex scientific terminology. My aim has been to minimise the use of jargon and to make the processes that have determined the shape of the landscape comprehensible to the average reader.

This has meant some simplification of the jargon and a pruning of the detail to a minimum. All the same we will, I'm afraid, have to deal with a minimal set of terms such as 'plate tectonics', 'reef limestone', 'landslides', 'scarp slope' and so on.

When I first use a piece of jargon I have put it in quote marks (for example, 'sandstone'). Many of these terms are defined in the Glossary, but I have also sometimes assumed that the meaning of a term is obvious from the context in which it appears.

While reading this book you may well find it useful to have open a large-scale map of the Lake District such as the OS 1:50,000 map (though the 1:25,000 map is essential for navigating on the ground). The 1:50,000 maps convey more easily an impression of the topography than the 1:25,000 maps, which are often crammed with vital navigational detail which can make it difficult to get an overview of the topography at a glance. Using a map while reading the book would also assist the reader to locate the places mentioned as examples (the index of place names at the back of the book includes grid references of places named in the text).

Photo 0.4 |

Narrowdale, a dry limestone valley in the foreground, with tilted sandstone and shale forming 'edges' in the central distance.

CHAPTER 1

Basement Blocks

A good place to start our look at the geology and scenery of the Peak District is atop the 'Shivering Mountain' Mam Tor, near Castleton. From the summit of Mam Tor there are superb all-round views of the Peak District's much-loved landscape and an excellent overview of the variety of the geology and scenery.

To the east, Mam Tor's flanks fall vertiginously away to a wide valley which to the south rises up sharply to a green rolling plateau. The steep slope leading to the upland area is broken in places by deep gashes, most notably to the south-south-east at Winnats (photo 1.1). The steep slope and the plateau are parts of an ancient sea bed where fragments of shells and other material collected, before being slowly turned into the amazing rock known as 'limestone'.

The steep slope marks the northern boundary of the 'White Peak', named after the light-grey colour of exposed limestone rocks. Limestone often produces fascinating scenery with an engaging range of unusual geological features. This may not be immediately obvious from this vantage point with the apparently featureless limestone uplands rolling off into the distance, unmarked apart from the deep gash of Winnats (photo 1.1). In later chapters we will encounter many of the fascinating geological features of limestone landscapes.

Photo 1.1 | The White Peak limestone plateau seen from the summit of Mam Tor; Winnats, upper centre.

To the north and east (and on Mam Tor underfoot too) the rocks are quite different. They were created from material eroded from highlands, carried down by rivers and dumped in the sea or lakes as sediments of sand and mud. These sediments slowly hardened into rocks known as 'sandstone' and 'shale'. Millions of years later these rocks underlie boggy, rolling moorland bounded by rocky edges and deeply incised valleys. The landscape is often flattish or slightly tilted with distinct steps and shelves (photo 1.2).

This is the Dark Peak, so-called after the dark peat exposed in the peat 'hags' that litter the wilder moorland and can make for difficult walking conditions (photo 3.1). The classic areas of such wilderness walking are Kinder Scout, here arrayed in all its glory just to the north, and beyond it Bleaklow and Black Hill. These are tough walking areas, offering vast vistas in good weather and will-sapping exposure when it is cold, wet or windy.

Photo 1.2 |

The southern edge of Kinder Scout seen from the summit of Mam Tor. The hummocky ground in the right foreground is a landslide.

But there is more to the Dark Peak's scenery than just peaty plateaux. Though not really visible from here, there are areas of more sandstone and shale to the west and east of the limestone, for example around high points such as Shining Tor, Shutlingsloe and the Roaches to the west, and Eyam Moor and Abney Moor to the east. These areas tend to have more valleys, a more insistently undulating landscape and have seen much of the lower land turned into pasture. This is the Dark Peak semi-tamed. Further east, running from north to south, are lines of 'edges' where tough, gritty rocks provide fine views, good walking and limitless opportunities for rock-climbing. These edges are another facet of the geology and scenery.

Before moving on it is important to mention a third set of rocks which can be found within the Peak District though not visible from our vantage point on top of Mam Tor. This group of rocks consists mostly of more sandstone and shale, but also has seams of 'coal' – ancient plant debris which did not decay but was turned into brittle, black, combustible rock. Some coal was mined in the Goyt Valley a few kilometres to the south-east of Mam Tor and in the area north-east of the Roaches. Many more coal-bearing beds are, of course, found outside the National Park boundaries on either side of the area. The rocks are less resistant than those of the White and Dark Peak, forming by and large lower ground (photo 4.1).

This brings us to another aspect of the landscape – the influence of humans. From Mam Tor the most obvious sign of human contribution to the view is without doubt the Hope Cement Works chimney stack. In certain light conditions, and with some squinting, it is possible to imagine it as a distant medieval cathedral spire (photo 1.3). Perhaps we can see it as a cathedral of praise to the industrial age. The other accoutrements of the human contribution are less intrusively conspicuous thanks to their familiarity, but are of no less significance: quarries, mine waste tips, improved fields, stonewalls and fences, farms, villages and towns, roads and ceaseless traffic, railways, electricity pylons, advertising signs for show caves and other attractions, plus legions of sheep and walkers, a smattering of cyclists and horse-riders, and the odd dust-raising posse of 4x4s and motorcyclists.

For good and bad, the Peak District landscape is a product of the interplay of geology and human activity. Its hills and valleys offer fantastic walking through an area of fascinating geology and intense human endeavour.

Photo 1.3 | The Hope valley and cement works chimney – looking, in particular light, rather like a distant cathedral spire.

Geologically speaking, the Peak District is the southern end of the Pennines and the whole Pennine range has a common geological history. In fact this geological history is shared with parts of Wales, much of Ireland and parts of north-western Europe and elsewhere. Each area has its own particular story to tell. We will be looking in a little more detail at the Peak District's own geo-biography in the following chapters, but it is useful to keep in mind that the geological forces shaping our area of interest shares some of its geological history with the wider region.

The earth is about 4,500 million years old. For most of its history, the earth's outer surface has been divided into a number of independent but interlocking 'tectonic plates'. These plates (continental and oceanic) are driven round the surface of the earth by convection currents within the earth, generated by the incredibly great heat of the earth's core. Over very long cycles (of about 500 million years) the continents tend to coalesce into one large 'supercontinent', then split up again into independent chunks of land mass. These individual chunks of continental plate are then driven around the surface of the earth, moving apart or scraping and sliding past each other or colliding and crashing until, once again, the continents join into a single supercontinent before breaking up and undergoing their long, slow global wandering all over again. The boundaries between tectonic plates are often the site of intense 'tectonic activity', with frequent earthquakes, volcanic eruptions and (where two continents collide) the building of mountains.

We will enter the story about 360 million years ago, when the continents were slowly joining together into a single supercontinent. The chunk of continental plate which underlies the Peak District today was then just south of the equator and moving slowly north. We can picture an area of mixed sea and land, with a great mountain range to the north and an arc of higher land to the south, jutting out from what is now the Brabant province of Belgium. This arc of higher land crossed the present-day southern North Sea, East Anglia, the south Midlands and most of Wales, fading away at the eastern coast of Ireland (map 1.1). This upland area is known to geologists as the Wales-Brabant High. Further south there was more land and here, as continents collided and collected, there was intense tectonic activity which affected our area. This tectonic activity caused some volcanic eruptions but these were minor events. The most important effect of the gathering of the continents on our area was a stretching of the continental plate, causing a period of sustained subsidence of the area over the next fifty million years (from about 360 until about 310 million years ago).

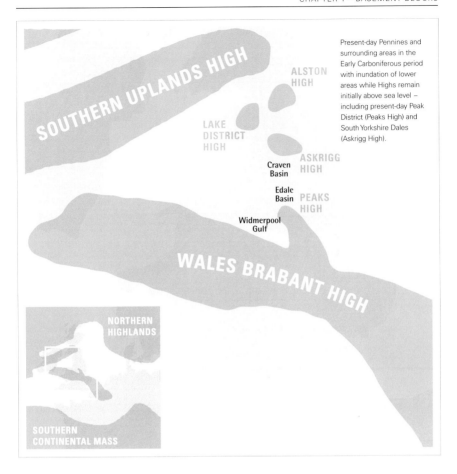

Map 1.1 | Present-day Pennines and surrounding areas in the Early Carboniferous period.

The present-day Peak District is centred around a small finger of high land, the Peaks High, that poked out from the Wales-Brabant High. It was bounded on its northern side by an area of lower land known to geologists as the Edale Basin and on its south-western flank by another low area, the Widmerpool Gulf. These 'highs' and 'basins' formed the highly uneven 'basement' on which the Peak District rocks were laid down between 360 and 300 million years ago. The boundaries between the highs and basins were marked by deep 'faults' or cracks in the underlying rocks, along which bits of land on either side could move up or down independently in response to stretching or compression of the underlying plate (diagram 1.1).

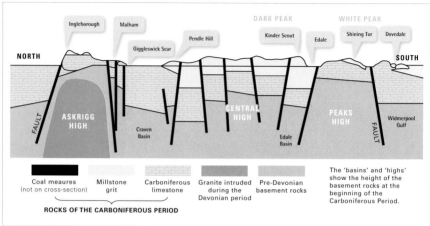

Diagram 1.1 (above) | Cross-section along the Pennines from the South Yorkshire Dales to the Peak District.

Finally it is worth taking a short peek into the frightful chasm of geological jargon. The earth's past is divided by geologists into a number of 'periods' (diagram 1.2). The periods in which the Pennine basement rocks were laid down are known as the 'Cambrian period', the 'Ordovician period' and the 'Silurian period'. Next along was the 'Devonian period' during which the Pennine area was above sea level and thus affected by erosion, so no new rocks were formed. The next period, from about 360 million years ago to 300 million years ago, is known as the 'Carboniferous period'; the events of which will be the subject of the next three chapters.

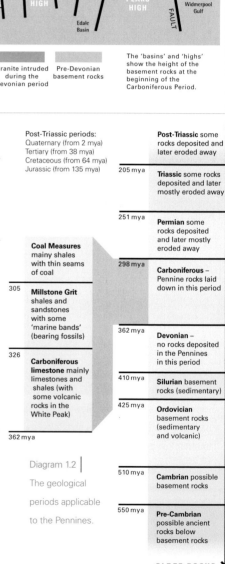

Diagram 1.2 | The geological periods applicable to the Pennines.

OLDER ROCKS

CHAPTER 2

Layers of Limestone

At first sight, it might seem that the area which is today the Peak District was a rather attractive environment during the Carboniferous period. The global climate was similar to that of modern times, but our chunk of continental plate was at a different point on the globe. The area then lay at the edge of a warm, shallow tropical sea just south of the equator. Life flourished in the sea water as waves lapped up on the idyllic sandy shore.

But the earth was a very different place. There was a much higher level of oxygen in the atmosphere than today. This meant that creatures that today are limited in size could grow much larger. So our tropical coast would have been home to dragonflies with wingspans of two or three metres, giant cockroaches, two-metre-long poisonous centipedes, massive scorpions, unpleasantly large spiders and other nightmarishly oversized beasts. All in all, it would have been pretty horrible for homo sapiens.

Map 2.1

Early Carboniferous period (Dinantian). The subsidence of underlying crust due to tectonic activity to the south led to the inundation of the large area of present day Britain, Ireland, north-west Europe and the North Sea. Under the water widespread limestone deposits were laid down, forming the Carboniferous Limestone.

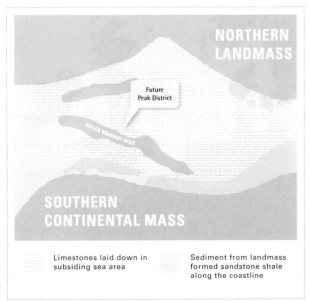

NORTHERN LANDMASS

Future Peak District

WALES BRABANT HIGH

SOUTHERN CONTINENTAL MASS

Limestones laid down in subsiding sea area

Sediment from landmass formed sandstone shale along the coastline

For most of the Carboniferous period the whole area experienced sustained subsidence as the underlying continental plate was stretched by tectonic forces to the south. This subsidence would probably have occurred in steps with the basins, bounded by faults, dropping further and further every so often. The basins were thus the first areas to fall beneath sea level, but even the highs were affected and fell underwater as the subsidence continued.

When the Peak High was first inundated it would have been only just under sea level, thus forming shallow, tropical seas where the sun's warming rays could penetrate with ease. Such sun-baked seas were essential for the biological and inorganic processes involved in the creation of limestone.

Making limestone

The various types of limestone found within the Peak District are gathered together under the general name of 'Carboniferous Limestone', a useful but misleading label. The Carboniferous tag simply means that these limestones were laid down in the Carboniferous period. All limestones contain carbon (in the form of 'calcium carbonate') whatever the geological period in which they were laid down, so the 'carboniferous' label adds nothing to our knowledge of the limestone except the period during which it was originally created.

Limestones are rocks containing a significant proportion of calcium carbonate (which is created by combining the commonly occurring natural mineral, calcium, with carbon dioxide). Pure limestone is 100 per cent calcium carbonate, but any rock made up with more than 50 per cent calcium carbonate is called a 'limestone' by geologists.

Some life forms create shells or skeletons from calcium carbonate. When they die, the shells fall to the sea bed where they are bored into by microscopic creatures which secrete calcium carbonate mud. The shells are also smashed to tiny fragments by currents and tides and become cemented together by the limestone mud. Algae and other micro-organisms create calcium carbonate 'mats' in which they live in colonies. When they move from an old mat to a new one the solid calcium carbonate filaments of the mat remain behind (and can form fossils – see Limestone fossils below).

Though the organic biological and biochemical processes of creating calcium carbonate usually dominate, it is also possible for it to be created inorganically. This can happen if the sea water is saturated with calcium and there is also a high rate of evaporation in a shallow sea under a hot sun. In these conditions calcium carbonate is directly deposited on the sea floor in tiny grains, which are rolled around by tides and currents, accreting more and more calcium carbonate to produce 'oolitic' limestone.

If it is very pure the limestone takes the crystalline form calcite (photo 5.13). Lumps of calcite crystals are often seen in natural scree, in material dumped onto quarry tracks and on waste tips, as well as by a very close look at some limestone exposures.

It will soon be obvious to anyone who looks at limestone outcrops within the White Peak that the rock is varied, with different colours and surface shape. This is because the nature of the limestone depends on the nature of the life forms in any particular area at any particular time. So the rock produced from an area where certain algae gather will be different from an area where shell fish predominate and so on. In one place corals may be common, while in another silica-rich sponges may dominate leading to the creation of silica 'chert' nodules within the limestone. Locations close to a beach would experience deposition of sand leading to the creation of patches of sandy limestone. The variations are limitless.

Over time, great thicknesses of various types of limestone were laid down on top of and around the Peaks High, building up a 'limestone platform'. These are the rocks that today are exposed at the surface in the area of the White Peak (and in the South Yorkshire Dales and other parts of Britain and western Europe).

Now this raises an intriguing question – if the sea was shallow why didn't the accumulating mass of calcium-carbonate matter soon pile up until it reached sea level and halted the process? The answer can only be that the sea bed subsided at a sustained rate over a long period. The rate of subsidence must have been just enough to keep the sea bed fairly close to sea level to allow the great thicknesses of limestone to accumulate. As we saw in the previous chapter, this generalised subsidence of the area was caused by tectonic forces stretching the continental plate on which our area rested, though other factors must also have played a part: for example, the accumulating weight of sediments depressing the underlying 'mantle'.

The subsidence was sustained over a long period, but it was not absolutely constant and continuous. There are very thin layers of soil and rootlets that have been discovered by geologists sandwiched between layers of limestone. The existence of these layers of soil, and also volcanic rocks that were clearly erupted onto surfaces above sea level, tell us that the top of the limestone did indeed sometimes emerge above sea level, for at least a short time, every now and again. However, the general picture was one where subsidence roughly kept pace with the rate at which the mass of calcium carbonate was being accumulated.

Photo 2.1 | Classic limestone outcrop, Lathkill Dale.

The limestone plateau is perhaps scenically restrained with an undulating surface and often with restricted views from higher points. However, with care and attention the detail of the landscape offers its own rewards. The main limestone of the White Peak is easy to identify exposed in numerous quarries and gorges such as Stoney Middleton, Chee Dale, Dovedale and the upper parts of Lathkill Dale, for example. The rocks are usually white to lightish grey, often with horizontal or gently dipping lines that seem to separate different layers or strata (photo 2.1).

However, seen in close-up the limestones are variable. There are as many different types of limestone as there are micro-environments and life forms in areas where it develops. All this means it is rather pointless trying to follow too closely the names given by geologists to the various formations of limestone in the area (such as Bee Low Limestones, the Woo Dale Limestones, Monsal Dale Limestones and Milldale Limestones). Their classifications are based on the study of small samples under a hand lens or microscope and then classification

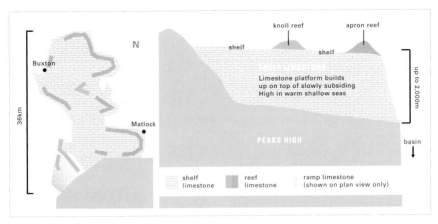

Diagram 2.1 | The Peaks high limestone platform and reefs.

under whatever system is currently in use (and the classification systems are ever-changing as geologists improve their understanding of their investigations).

For the walker, rather than trying to analyse the close details of different limestones, we can use a fairly simple system to classify limestone according to the environment in which it was laid down. Diagram 2.1 illustrates major types of environment within a 'limestone platform': 'shelf', 'knoll reef', 'apron reef', 'slope', 'ramp' and, off the platform, 'basin'.

Initially it was the basins surrounding most of the Peaks High that were inundated and subject to the accumulation of sedimentation, with only thin, impure limestones mixed with a high proportion of mud and sand. Once the Peaks High had subsided below sea level, 'shelf limestones' were laid down in a lagoon environment on the top of the high. These are generally very pure limestones – in places as much as 98.5 per cent calcium carbonate.

The limestones were laid down on top of one another, building up the platform layer by layer. They can often be seen in slices, cut through the limestone in quarries and railway cuttings as well as some of the natural limestone gorges. This layering is a key feature of the shelf limestones, with horizontal or slightly dipping stratification which can usually be seen. This is known as 'bedding', as in photos 2.2, 2.3, 2.4 and 2.5. It usually represents some sort of break or change in the process of sedimentation (for example change in the rate of deposition or the content of the sedimentary material); the break becomes etched into the rocks as a (usually) horizontal line. Sedimentary rocks are often made up of a series of such beds laid on top of one another. Beds can be 'thin' or 'thick' or anywhere in between (although extremely thin bedding is known as 'lamination'). Bedding may also be absent, in which case the rock is said to be 'massive'.

However, it is now thought that at least some of the bedding seen in the limestone was caused by internal processes during 'lithification' (being turned from loose sediment to solid rock), rather than due to breaks in the process of sedimentation.

Other lines, usually near-vertical, are also often seen in limestone crags and quarry faces, but these are not bedding. Photo 2.4 shows a quarry face with bedding at the top of the crags and massive, unbedded limestone forming the bulk of the cliff. However, large numbers of vertical lines are clearly visible. These are drying-out 'joints' created shortly after the limestone was laid down and contracted slightly as water was forced out of the mass of limestone sediment.

Photo 2.2 | Bedding in shelf limestone at Railway cutting, High Peak Trail, Middleton.

Photo 2.3 | Bedding in shelf limestone at Miller's Dale Quarry, Wye Valley.

Photo 2.4 | Bedding is seen at the top of the quarry face, but not in the main face though vertical 'joints' are prominent, Middle Peak Quarry, National Stone Centre, Wirksworth.

Photo 2.5 | Tilted bedding in shelf limestone seen in quarry face, Dene Quarry, Middleton.

Photo 2.6 | Downfold in thinly bedded dark ramp limestone, Manifold valley.

Bedding may well not be horizontal. If it is seen at some other angle then it usually means that tectonic forces have folded or tilted the rocks (photo 2.5) but, in some cases, especially limestone reefs, the original bedding may have dipped downwards when it was laid down. Where tilting is evident, it is usually a gentle dip in one direction or the other. In a very few places it may be folded quite dramatically, such as at Apes Tor on the River Manifold (photos 2.6, 5.3 and w7.5). The causes of such folding are covered in chapter 5.

Another feature that can be seen in various places in the shelf limestone is 'chert' in the form of nodules that look like big pebbles embedded in the limestone. This is a silica-rich flinty rock that was formed from clumps of silica-rich sponges (a very basic form of multi-cellular life). The nodules of chert are uncommon but can be seen in some railway cuttings and quarry faces, for example on walk 14 on an old railway line west of Wirksworth (photo 2.7). Another location at which they can be seen is in caverns, usually sticking out of the limestone and of a different colour such as Blue John cavern (photo 2.8) where they are quite impressive.

Limestone reefs are another feature of the limestone platform. Reefs form some of the most dramatic hills and scenery of the White Peak, including Upper Dovedale (Chrome Hill – photos w5.1 and w5.4) and Lower Dovedale (Thorpe Cloud – photo w8.1) and around Castleton (Winnats and Cave Dale – photo w13.5). Geologists are not entirely sure how these ancient reefs were created. They are made up of a limestone mud produced by micro-organisms and algae. The mud must have solidified very quickly, perhaps because a sticky film created by other secretions of micro-organisms covered the outside of the growing reef, thus preventing

Photo 2.7 | Chert nodules in limestone outcrop, Middleton.

Photo 2.8 | Chert nodules in a limestone cavern.

it from being washed away by currents. Limestone can cement particles together very quickly indeed. Once built, the reefs rapidly became home to a variety of life forms and the present-day outcrops often display an abundance of fossils (although the reef itself is essentially made up of solidified limestone mud), although in many places no fossils are visible in the reefs.

Geologists distinguish two types of reef in the Peak District, 'apron reefs' and 'knoll reefs' (diagram 2.1). These geological phenomena have accumulated their own veritable mound of different names (see the appendix on geological terms). We will stick with apron reef and knoll reef as these have been used in previous publications and guides on the area, though it is worth noting that knoll reefs are sometimes known as 'mud mounds'; while this is not such an exotic name it is fairly accurate.

Apron reefs form around the edge of the limestone platform, perhaps as a result of wave action, but there is no agreement on the way muddy limestone can raise itself up into such a mound. The reefs of upper Dovedale, such as Chrome Hill and Parkhouse Hill (photos 0.1, w5.1 and w5.4), are apron reefs, as are those seen in Cave Dale and Winnats. Photo 2.9 shows an apron reef near Mam Tor, Snels Low (1135 8180, opposite Eldon Hill quarry). It is one of a series of such hills, gradually becoming smaller, that extend the arc of apron reefs south-west of Winnats. Although quite small Snels Low is quite distinctive and shapely, mimicking to some degree the form of Chrome Hill and Parkhouse Hill.

Photo 2.9 | Apron reef, now an isolated hill, Snels Low, near Castleton.

Apron reefs are somewhat complex structures with a 'fore-reef' and a 'back-reef' lying over the main algal reef. Reefs do not usually display bedding, although at times it is possible to distinguish bedding on fore-reefs and back-reefs. In such cases it is usually relatively thin bedding and tilts downwards at the same angle as when it was laid down on the edge of the growing carbonate platform; its tilt is not a result of tectonic movements as is the case with tilted bedding in the main shelf limestone. An example of this can be seen in the narrow entrance to Cave Dale (photo 2.10) and also looking up at the reef limestone below Peveril Castle once you have entered the dale proper (walk 13). Higher up Cave Dale, where it narrows to a gorge only 1.5 metres wide at ground level, the beds can be seen tilting in the other direction (to the south). This is bedding in the back-reef.

The apron reefs formed a rim, though not a continuous one, around the edge of the main limestone platform. They created a lagoon environment, helping retain limestone sediments on the shelf and thus allowing it to be built up and not washed away. Beyond the apron reefs the seabed fell steeply (the 'slope' of the limestone platform) to the deep basin. There were channels created at the time between the apron reefs which allowed material to escape and settle on the slope. To the south-west of the present-day White Peak the platform was not rimmed by apron reefs and a steep slope, but the limestone platform descended more gently towards the Widmerpool Gulf on the 'ramp' of the limestone platform. This is what happened around the lower Dove and Manifold valleys in the south-west of the White Peak, with material being washed down into the Widmerpool Gulf to form dark, impure limestones.

Photo 2.10

Upper part of the rock exposure shows thin bedding tilting to lower right (north) in the fore-reef just inside Cave Dale.

Knoll reefs were formed within the main platform lagoon and in slightly deeper water where there were no photosynthetic algae but mats of fine lime sediment were trapped to form these mud mounds. Many knoll reefs form prominent scenic features. The Dovedale and Manifold valleys in the south of the White Peak are cut into knoll reefs, forming some of the scenic highlights of the Peak District, including Wetton Hill, Narrowdale Hill (photo w7.3), Thorpe Cloud (photo w8.1) and Bunster Hill. These reefs were formed on the slope down to the Widmerpool Gulf and are frequently surrounded by dark, impure limestones.

Not all knoll reefs have left a distinct mark on the landscape. A cluster of more than 15 knoll reefs surrounds the village of Monyash. None has much effect on the skyline, though some form slightly higher points (such as Bole Hill, 184 676). However, even some of these knoll reefs can be detected by local scenic effects. The dry, gorge-like narrow section of Lathkill Dale near Ricklow Quarry is cut through one of these very tough knoll reef limestones. Another example is a very minor knoll reef near the confluence of the Lathkill and Bradford rivers (2185 6435). Although it is hardly a speck on the 1:25,000 geology map (and is not marked at all on the 1:50,000 geology map) it forms a distinct rock face rising vertically out of the surrounding lower land (photo 2.11).

Thus we have a picture of a mass of limestone accumulating in the teeming tropical sea, slowly building up a platform whose top remained largely just below sea level while the underlying area slowly subsided. However, this subsidence was not entirely steady and continuous, occurring instead in fits and jerks. Certainly there were some periods when the top of the platform was above sea level and some erosion took place; soil and vegetation also took hold for a short time, before further subsidence reintroduced the sea. Some fossil rootlets and plant matter have been found by geologists within the limestone recording these interludes.

We will return to limestone in a later chapter to see how and why it has its own very singular set of landscape features – dry valleys, gorges, sink holes, caverns and cave systems. However, before moving away from the story of the creation of the limestone rocks, we need to add some extra detail to the general story.

Photo 2.11 | Minor knoll reef forming almost vertical outcrop in otherwise low terrain, Alport.

Limestone fossils

The bulk of the limestone in the Peak District is made up of microscopic shell fragments or secretions of calcium carbonate, not whole fossils. Usually it is impossible to see any fossils or recognisable fragments, even with the aid of some extra-strong reading glasses. However there are places in the limestone where easily visible fragments or even fairly complete fossils of animals and plants are found, and sometimes in abundance. Recognisable fossils of a wide range of creatures can be seen: algae, corals, sponges, bryozoans, brachiopods, gastropods, trilobites, ostracods and echinoderms.

The last category included a type of animal life form known as crinoid. Crinoids lived in vast numbers, attached to the seabed, sifting food out of the passing waters. They look like plants but can be considered as somewhat like a present-day starfish tethered by one limb. The ring-like remains of crinoid limbs are probably the most common easily visible fossil type in the Peak District today (photos 2.12 and 2.13) and can be exceptionally beautiful in polished rock (as seen in quite a few places in footpaths and stiles).

The rings were held together by soft tissue which decayed when the animal died leaving the mass of harder rings; these then get washed around by tides and currents getting mixed up with limestone mud. Some outcrops of limestone, when looked at closely, are just a mass of crinoid and other fragments cemented together to form the solid rock. In a few places whole crinoids have fallen to the sea bed after dying

Photo 2.12 | Crinoid fragments.
The large fragment is 2.5cm long.

Photo 2.13 | Cross-section through crinoid (2.5cm diameter).

somewhere with no tides or currents, and so the fragments have not been scattered and mixed up to any great extent. In such situations, although the surviving remains are not connected and might be slightly displaced, it is possible to see what it might have looked like. The best place to see this is in an exposure of rock in an old quarry at the National Stone Centre near Wirksworth, as illustrated in photo w14.2.

Furthermore it is relatively common to see parts or even whole shell fossils. These are easy to spot if the shell flutings are visible (photos 2.14 and 2.15). Sometimes, however, they are seen in profile rather than from above. In such situations the fossils look like small 'saucer' shapes. Sometimes these saucers can be quite dense, often appearing to be loosely stacked on top of each other or perhaps looking as if a load of them had been dumped in a viscous fluid (photos 2.16 and 2.17). A very impressive

Photo 2.14 | Brachiopod fragments (width of view 10cm).

Photo 2.15 | Brachiopod (width of fossil 40cm).

Photo 2.16 | Brachiopod fragments (width of view 15cm).

Photo 2.17 | Gigantoproductus collection, Ricklow Quarry (width of view 1.25m).

collection of fossils of a large shell form known as 'gigantoproductus' can be seen in the quarry face at Ricklow Quarry and in fallen blocks (photo 2.17). It is very risky to approach the quarry face, but the pattern can be distinguished from a reasonable distance (walk 12). A less impressive collection, but vastly safer to take a close look at, can be seen in the National Stone Quarry (walk 14).

As well as shell fragments, quite a bit of the Peak District limestone (especially the 'reef limestone') has been created by micro-organisms. Some of these bore into the shell fragments and secrete a form of 'carbonate' or 'limestone mud'. Algae also secrete limestone mud as a form of encrusting layers which survives after the colony of algae has moved on or died.

One reasonably common type of fossil comes from colonies of simple, single-celled, blue-green algae (one of the oldest known forms of life stretching back to about 3.5 billion years ago). It forms structures known as 'stromatolites'. The living colonies or beds of algae are structured in layers or mats, with each layer representing a growth phase of the colony. The algae build these thread-like filaments by precipitating the calcium-carbonate mats within which thrive colonies of photosynthetic and non-photosynthetic microbes. When an inundation of sediment or mud is caught up in the outer mat the organisms slough off their sticky sheaths and glide upwards to a new surface and create a new layer.

This growth pattern causes the layering seen in the fossils in photos 2.18 and 2.19. These have sometimes been called 'layered stones'. They can vary in size consid-

Photo 2.18 + 2.19 | Fossilised algal growth patterns (stromatolites) (width of view 10cm and 35cm).

erably, from the size of golf ball to that of a small garden shed and have no specific structure. This is because in strong currents they are elongated parallel to the direction of water flow. In stiller waters they form rounded 'bun' structures. This is how many textbooks and guides tend to illustrate them – but this doesn't help when what you find out in the field are the stringy versions. At times it might be slightly difficult to distinguish between these twisting algal fossils and patches of dense numbers of large brachiopod fossils, while at other times these algal fossils can look a bit like standard bedding. Examples of algal fossils can be found on and below the summit areas of Chrome Hill (walk 5), High Wheeldon (walk 6), below Treak Cliff (walk 13) and many other places.

In large sections of the White Peak, especially around Matlock and to its west, the calcium carbonate of the limestone has been chemically transformed into magnesium carbonate, forming a rock known as 'dolomite' (photo 8.3). Geologists are not certain when, how or why this happened, but it is possible that it occurred soon after the rocks were initially formed. The 'dolomitised' rock has weathered to a brownish colour and outcrops in a few places as 'tors' or clumps of isolated rocks at high points (such as Harboro Rocks, walk 14). Apart from the tors, in general it is scenically unemphatic.

We also need to introduce some discord and disturbance into this picture of the millions of years of quiet sedimentation, accumulation and lithification of calcium carbonate into the varied limestones of our gently subsiding area. Now and then things were not so gentle and more violent features have left their mark on the Peak District. The volcanic activity, generated by clashing tectonic plates to the south of our area, affected our area occasionally. A variety of volcanic rocks were erupted onto the surface in the form of lavas and 'pyroclastic' fragments. Thus the geological maps of today show a series of lavas, 'tuffs' and 'vent agglomerates' in the White Peak area. Lavas are rocks produced by molten magma flowing onto the earth's surface as molten lava. Tuffs are rocks produced by pyroclastic eruptions of 'volcanic ash'. Vent agglomerates are the remains of molten magma that did not reach the surface, but was stuck in the 'vent' on its way to the surface. Today, in some areas in the Peak District, the rocks of these ancient volcanic events are exposed on the surface.

Some of the lavas are identifiable by geologists as having erupted above sea level, so the volcanic record reminds us that at times the top of the accumulating limestone platform poked out above sea level. The volcanic outcrops are fairly few and far between. They form long thin streaks largely concentrated in two areas; west of Matlock Bath and east of Buxton. Though there are few actual outcrops on the surface, these volcanic rocks have left a clear signature on the scenery in several places as hills. The hard volcanic rocks often form high points in the present-day relief, such as at Masson Hill, west of Matlock Bath. Elsewhere the volcanic rocks may be seen as an edge sticking up in the middle of limestone territory (photo w15.1). The line of volcanic rocks stretching south from Miller's Dale forms a twisting edge of a run of higher ground, running from north to south along the eastern side of Blackwell Dale, then swinging east to west along Sough Top, Calton Hill and Chelmorton Low and then swinging roughly north to south through Nether Low and Great Low. It thus appears in some places as an edge or slope and in other places as distinct hills.

A point of terminology: Chelmorton Low, Nether Low and Great Low are all high points, not low points as you might be led to expect from their names. Low is an old English word for a low hill, one that rises up above the surrounding land, but not very high. Chelmorton Low is actually a very distinct hill with a sharp, steep eastern 'scarp' slope (see walk 15). Interestingly, these three 'lows' are also the sites of pre-historic cairns and tumuli (and there is a chambered cairn about a kilometre east of Chelmorton Low).

We have now built up our picture of the world where the rocks of the Carboniferous Limestone came into existence and what those rocks look like today when exposed on the surface. For millions upon millions of years minute quantities of calcium carbonate accumulated on the sea bed, produced by organisms and by inorganic processes, there turning into great thicknesses of rock, occasionally rudely interrupted by incursions of volcanic rock. This is essentially the story of how the White Peak rocks were laid down.

CHAPTER 3

Grains of Grit

The name says it all: 'Millstone Grit'. The very words carry an image of the rough vertebrae of England's mountainous spine, and remind us also of the gritty spirit of the hardy people who determinedly eked out a fragile living in the hostile highland conditions. No other geological name in Britain is more evocative of its present-day environment. For geologists, however, the Millstone Grit is simply the name given to rocks deposited on top of the Carboniferous Limestone.

Much of the scenery of the Millstone Grit areas of the South Pennines and the northern stretches of the Peak District (known as the Dark Peak) is harsh. Here is some of the toughest walking in England, across such rain-sodden, wind-blasted, mud-blanketed moorland as Kinder Scout (photos 1.2, 3.1, 3.3 and photos for walk 1), Bleaklow (bleak indeed in all but the best of weather) and Black Hill (named after its muddy black soil). These are areas with few rock outcrops, but plenty of peat bog and soggy wet ground. It is a landscape of stark beauty, though it is a beauty that is not always immediately apparent to the weather-battered walker. It takes grit to walk, work or live among these wild hills.

Photo 3.1 | View over Kinder Scout plateau from Kinder Low.

However, not all Millstone Grit scenery fits this gritty description and we will see some tamed areas also, where green fields jostle for dominance with moorland and where prosperous-looking stone farmhouses pepper the slopes (photo w2.5). The Millstone Grit scenery is not all gritty. In fact, the Millstone Grit rocks are not all grits. They are a mix of different types of sedimentary rocks known as 'sandstone', 'siltstone' and 'shale', with only some outcrops of 'grit' (which is simply another name for coarse sandstone). The differentiating factor between these types of sedimentary rock is the size of the eroded mineral grains that form the sediments that make up the rock. Very small particles form shale (or 'mudstone'), medium-sized ones form siltstone and larger ones sandstone.

As the name implies, at least some of the rocks of this group were used for making millstones. Fortunately or unfortunately, the name expanded to cover not just the beds used for millstones, but all the grits, sandstones and shales laid down on top of the Carboniferous Limestone until the time of the next group of rocks, the Coal Measures. This is a shame as grit and shale are, shall we say, like chalk and cheese. Their very different characteristics are what lie behind the scenery of the Dark Peak.

Certainly the sandstone and grit are the most conspicuous of the Millstone Grit rocks, forming the rocky 'edges' that characterise much of the Dark Peak scenery (photo 3.2 and photos for walks 1, 9, 10 and 11). This is because of the resistant nature of sandstone and grit which are not easily eroded. The sandstones and grits of the Millstone Grit are divided by geologists into a number of 'formations' the Mam Tor Beds, Shale Grit, Kinderscout Grit, Five Clouds Sandstones, Roaches Grit and Chatsworth Grit (to name the main formations; there are several subsidiary formations).

Photo 3.2

Shining Edge, Shining Tor;
Shutlingsloe in distance.

However, shale is the antithesis of grit. It is easily eroded away and belies the tough gritty image of the Millstone Grit label. It is made up of very tiny fragments of eroded material. This small size of fragment would normally result in a mudstone, but shale also includes some organic matter. This is usually only between three and five percent of the total mass of the rock, but it means that shale and mudstone have very different characteristics. Shale is usually 'laminated' into very thin layers (effectively a form of bedding). It is usually 'friable' and can often be crumbled by hand, while mudstone shows no such lamination and is harder.

Photo 3.3 | Crumbling shale beds, stream side exposure, Goldsitch area.

Photo 3.4 | Shale being eroded away between two beds of sandstone, Back Tor.

While the sandstone and grit are exposed to view in the rocky edges, out on the hills there are generally few exposures of shale. It seldom peers through the covering vegetation and, when it does, it is usually just a small, dark muddy-looking mess on the banks of a stream and easily missed. Nonetheless, in several of the walks (numbers 1, 2, 3, 7, 9 and 11) shale outcrops can be seen. In all these places the shale is seen crumbling away and, in several instances, it has patches that are slumped and broken. At some locations it is clear that the shale is being eroded away underneath overhanging sandstone – foretelling of a rock fall or river-side collapse to come.

It is precisely this mix of tough, resistant grit and sandstone and weak, friable shale that determines so much of the scenery and geomorphology of the Dark Peak as we will see in the remainder of this chapter and also in chapter 6 (where we look at landslides caused by the interlayering of sandstone and shale).

Making deltas

Geologists estimate that the modern-day Mississippi gives a good idea of the size of the river transporting material down from the north of our area. The river system, on reaching the sea, built out a delta on top of the Carboniferous Limestone, smothering all of it with mineral sediments. The delta of this great river covered much of what is present-day northern and western Europe. On reaching the delta, the big river split into 'distributary' channels. Each distributary pushed out into the sea, often building natural levees, then dumped material along and at the end of the channel.

The channel would thus slowly build upwards and outwards as a 'lobe' of low-lying land; a landscape of flood plains, marshes, tidal flats and lakes. At some point, probably during a flood flow, the distributary breached its levees some way back, finding a new, steeper, shorter route to the sea. The new channel would eventually extend out progressively to form a new lobe. This is a process known as 'channel diversion'. Over time a series of overlapping lobes were built up and out (diagram 3.3).

One feature often seen in the rocky edges is called 'cross bedding'. This type of bedding is not the standard horizontal or gently tilted bedding seen in limestone

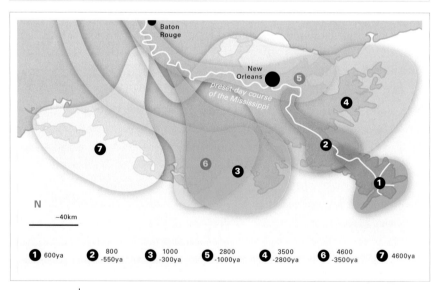

Diagram 3.3 | Delta lobe build out on the Mississippi.

valleys and quarries. On individual boulders and tors on the rocky edges the bedding runs in a series of curved lines, often cut off at the top by another series of curved lines at a different angle. This curved bedding is produced by fast currents typical of those found in powerful river channels. The cutting across one set of curved beds by a later set is the result of the river channel shifting place. Cross bedding is very obvious on some edges such as Kinder Scout (walk 1), Millstone Edge and Stanage Edge (both on walk 9, photo w9.4) and the Roaches (walk 11, photos w11.1 and w11.4).

Another important facet of the Millstone Grit rocks is their 'cyclic' nature with layers of sandstone followed by shale, followed by sandstone, shale and so on. Within our area the different layers of shale and sandstone are repeatedly found on top of one another in cycles, with each cycle representing a new lobe of the delta being built out. At first only the very finest mud particles were carried far out, but as the distributary channel moved forwards medium-fine particles of silt were carried out and dumped. As the lobe was built out, it was sand that was being dumped. Across the Pennines there are a dozen or more separate sandstone layers, with intervening shales (and also siltstones).

Some rock formations within the Millstone Grit are more varied with rapid changes between sandstone and shale, such as the Mam Tor Beds (photos w3.4 and w3.5).

The deposits of material that formed the Millstone Grit Group rocks originally covered the entire area, including the areas where limestone forms the surface rock today. The rock covering of Millstone Grit has been eroded away above the White Peak and also the South Yorkshire Dales, exposing the underlying limestone.

The Chatsworth Grit, for example, forms the long line of impressive rocky edges on the eastern side of the Peaks known as Derwent Edge, Stanage Edge, Millstone Edge and Curbar Edge. It also forms a less prominent edge in the south-western corner of the Peaks, known as Gradbach Hill (walk 11). This particular edge is over-shadowed by its neighbouring edge, the Roaches, which is particularly impressive. The fact that the same Chatsworth Grit appears at the surface on both sides of the area strongly suggests that it was once a horizontal layer that covered the whole of the area between the eastern and western edges and that, after being slightly folded up, most of it eroded away. The remaining edges remind us that the delta once covered hundreds of square kilometres of the entire region and beyond.

Perhaps the best known of the Dark Peak hills is Kinder Scout. It was mass trespass actions on Kinder Scout in the 1930s that sparked off the political movement for gaining access to these previously forbidden areas. This also resulted in the creation in the late 1940s of Britain's National Parks (of which the Peak District was the first) and, more recently, of the 'right to roam' access legislation which has opened up even more stretches of the Dark Peak (and indeed some parts of the White Peak) to access by walkers. It is all too easy when we stride out across access land to forget the effort it took to open it up for us.

Kinder Scout's gently tilting summit plateau is the highest point in the Dark Peak. The wide open boggy moorland is more than 600 metres high over an area of some 5 kilometres east to west and 3 kilometres north to south – even though the summit itself reaches only 636 metres in height. The summit plateau is capped by a highly resistant layer of grit, known as the Kinderscout Grit. It forms the marvellous edges on the southern, eastern and northern rims of the summit plateau (walk 1). The great size of the fairly flattish summit plateau means that once you get away from the edges views are extremely limited, even from the 'summit', which can be a challenge to locate. Indeed, even in good clear weather navigation away from the edges is challenging. In misty weather it is downright demanding of navigational ability (photo 3.1).

The flattish summit plateau results in a 'stepped' scenery on the flanks, with 'shelves' and 'steps' visible in the flanks of the mountain (photo 3.5 and diagram 3.1). The easily eroded shale underlies the shelves and sandstone/grit forms the steps.

Bleaklow and Black Hill, north of Kinder Scout, are even more bleak. There are no rocky edges to offer a slightly less traumatic walking experience in bad weather, and there are very few rock outcrops to draw the interest of walkers who want to learn a bit about the geology of the scenery they are walking through. The bogs are bigger and tougher and the navigation much more challenging (even in clear weather) than Kinder Scout. All the same, walking these hills is supremely rewarding offering the opportunity to appreciate what remains, despite some human intervention, of a wilderness in the close environs of major urban areas.

This is a landscape of rolling hills with a multitude of small streamlets flowing outwards in all directions from the highest points, coalescing into a few larger valleys which cut into the mountain massif. The soil is thin and impoverished, supporting heather, bilberry and grasses. The views on all these hills are limited to the great expanses of moorland and wide open skies.

To the east and south of Kinder Scout the Millstone Grit landscape is subtly different. There is a long zone running from north to south of long rocky edges, some stretching for several kilometres from north to south, broken and indented only by faults and folds. The

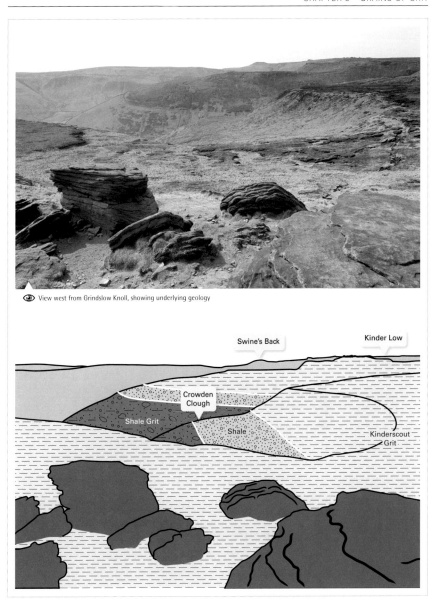

👁 View west from Grindslow Knoll, showing underlying geology

Diagram 3.1 + Photo 3.5 | Shelf and step topography on Kinder Scout.

View west from Grindslow Knoll, showing underlying geology.

edges are usually tilted with a gentle slope dipping down from the top of the edge, often to another edge. Indeed in places it is clear that there are several edges, one after the other. The steep rocky edges are known as 'scarp slopes' or 'scarps' and the gentle slopes as 'dip slopes', producing scarp and dip topography. This tilting is the result of later tectonic activity which has slightly arched the beds of the Millstone Grit (chapter 5); where the beds remain horizontal the effect is to produce 'step and shelf' topography.

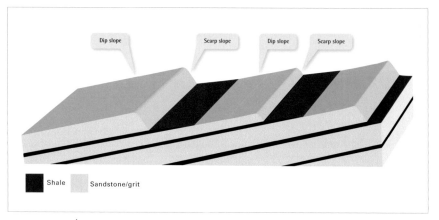

Diagram 3.2 | Scarp and dip slopes.

To name just a few of the more outstanding examples we can note Derwent Edge, Stanage Edge, Millstone Edge (photos for walk 9) and Curbar Edge (photos for walk 10). These are all in fact part of the same edge running on and off over 15 kilometres in a line of rocky crags, often smattered with climbers and topped with walkers. The rock forming the edge is known as the 'Chatsworth Grit'. This rather reverses the usual situation where walkers look up to see climbers – along the rocky edges you can frequently peer down at climbers getting up to your level the hard way.

The rough grits of the edges are notorious for ripping into frail skin and flesh as climbers place their entire weight on two or three fingers jammed into tiny cracks. Some of Britain's great rock climbers such as Joe Brown and (the decidedly gritty) Don Whillans first learnt their skills on the grit edges. They also offer hillwalkers many of the Dark Peak's scenic gems and, while they can provide some of the toughest walking conditions possible in stormy weather, they can also introduce the discerning hillwalker to some spectacularly impressive scenery.

From Curbar Edge, the view west is to the grassy limestone plateau with its verdant dry valleys (and glimpses of quarry). To the north and south, the view is of the rocky edge running off into the distance. To the east it is of flattish moorland, interrupted by the odd up-turned edge rolling off into the distance and with hints of 'urbania' beyond. The skies are wide open, but the views are of contrasts east and west and underline the significant role played by the underlying geology in the present-day scenery.

On the western side there are fewer rocky edges, instead the scenery is marked by less steep, vegetated edges which punctuate the skyline. Axe Edge, standing imperiously over the upper reaches of the River Dove (walk 4), exemplifies the western edge scenery with its absence of exposed rock. A few kilometres to the north Shining Edge (photo 3.2) is also vegetated, but there is a tiny rocky edge which offers fine views of the area to the south-west around the shapely form of Shutlingsloe (also a magnificent viewpoint in itself as well as being highly attractive to look at). South of Shining Tor there are several small, isolated rock outcrops that break the surface as remnants of a rocky edge. Further south there are two superb rocky edges – the Roaches and Ramshaw Rocks (photos 3.6 and 3.7 and photos for walk 11).

Photo 3.6 | Ramshaw Rocks, dip and scarp slope almost indistinguishable except for clear tilt of bedding from upper right to lower left.

Photo 3.7 | Ramshaw Rocks, improbable rock sculpture.

Smaller and less intimidating moors than those of Bleaklow and Black Hill are found in the Millstone Grit areas to the west and east of the White Peak. Abney Moor is a good place to get a feel for moorland walking without the same physical and navigational effort demanded by the more massive moors to the north (walk 2).

This is a more subdued landscape of mixed moor and field (if only for pasture) and of isolated stone farmhouses. The moorlands that remain are remnant patches of what was once a much more extensive area. Enclosure and attempts at farming started in earnest in the 18th and 19th centuries though some areas, for example around Bretton, are of medieval origin.

The 'stepped' nature of the landscape is still easily visible in this more restrained scenery. There are even a few small rocky edges to be seen producing in places a rather compacted Dark Peak landscape experience, for example at the western end of Bretton Clough (walk 2).

The low leonine hill called Abney Low is a classic example of this more moderate scenery, considerably modified by human influence. The layered nature of the hill is easily discerned with flat areas separated by short sharp rises (photo w2.5). The whole of Abney Low is agricultural land, grass pasture divided into fields by a grid of dead straight stonewalls with a substantial old farm sitting at its centre.

The Millstone Grit rocks were laid down in an expanding river delta, draining from the north into the subsiding sea. The sediments that formed the rock were dumped in freshwater lakes, but there were a few occasions when relative sea levels rose and the delta area was inundated by the sea. This short-lived incursions are recorded in thin 'marine bands' containing marine fossils which enable geologists to work out the time relationship between the different rocks of the Millstone Grit in our area and elsewhere.

On the other hand, as well as incursions of the sea, there were times when the area temporarily built up far enough above the sea level to form swamps in which a very special type of rock (coal) was formed. Only a few very thin coal seams were laid down in the upper parts of the Millstone Grit, but their appearance tells us that the environment was changing once again and foretold of bigger changes to come.

CHAPTER 4

Lingering Lignin

The third great group of rocks within the Carboniferous period is known as the Coal Measures. The coal that turned Britain into the world's first fossil fuel-powered industrial nation was dug from the rocks of this group (which outcrop in the Midlands and North of England, the lowlands of Scotland, and in the valleys of South and North-East Wales) .

However, just as with the Carboniferous Limestone and Millstone Grit labels, the 'Coal Measures' name is rather misleading. The coal is found in thin seams, usually no more than a metre or two thick and often much thinner (and indeed some very thin beds of coal are found in the Millstone Grit). These coal seams actually form only a very small proportion of the rocks of the Coal Measures, which are generally our old friends sandstone and shale, along with occasional 'marine bands'.

The Coal Measures rocks within the Peak District (as defined by the National Park boundaries) are concentrated to the west and south-west of Buxton in the Goyt valley area and in the Gradbach/Goldsitch area (photo 4.1). However, just as the Millstone Grit once covered the whole of the limestone areas of the Pennines, so too did the Coal Measures Group blanket the entire area on top of the Millstone Grit rocks. The rocks of the Coal Measures have been severly eroded, leaving only a small area of Coal Measures rocks within the National Park area.

Photo 4.1 | Subdued landscape of the Coal Measures near Goldsitch (horizontal across centre of photo, beyond stone wall) with Millstone Grit edges on the skyline.

The coal was laid in an ancient swampy tropical forest, which was still part of our major river drainage system, but slightly closer inland from the edge of the advancing delta lobes. We can imagine a very complex terrain of shifting river channels, swamps and lakes. The river channels were lined by natural levees or banks, occasionally breached by floods. There were also occasional incursions of seawater.

The first trees would have populated the levees and any dry ground between the river channels. Other plants grew in the swampy ground. As plants died their debris collected in the swampy ground. Coal is formed when plant debris gathers and is not subject to decay, but is transformed initially into peat and then coal (see below).

Photo 4.2

Coal – compressed plant debris that was preserved from decay and then heated and subjected to pressure for several tens of millions of years in order to be turned into coal. Width of view 10cm.

It used to be thought that the accumulating plant debris must have been protected from decay by very rapid burial. This smothering kept out the oxygen needed by the micro-organisms that carry out the chemical processes of recycling dead vegetable matter. Thus the organic matter was preserved and the coal-forming processes could take place.

This view is now being reconsidered. The Carboniferous period saw the development of the first true forests, though not with trees that would be familiar to us. Horsetails grew up to 10 metres high, as did tree ferns and tree-sized clubmosses. The first real trees were 'lycophytes' which could grow to 30 metres high and up to 1.5 metres in diameter. These trees did not have branches like today's specimens, but supported a canopy growing out of the top of the tree trunk.

These were the first plants to overcome the problem of how to grow tall. They achieved this by developing a tough supportive bark. These first trees had a much higher ratio of 'bark to wood' than modern trees – 8 to 1 or even 20 to 1 for the earliest trees as against 1 to 4 in today's species. The major component of bark is a substance known as 'lignin'. It is an 'organic polymer' and plays an important role in the carbon cycle, sequestrating atmospheric carbon into the living tissues of woody plants (and releasing it during decay). It is, furthermore, important in conducting water through plant stems, and it fills the gaps between cell walls and cellulose, providing mechanical strength to the plant and thus allowing it to grow taller.

Photo 4.3 | The Roaches sycnline (Ramshaw Rocks left foreground, Thorpe Cloud centre, the Roaches right skyline); Coal Measures below the Roaches, centre right.

Another property of lignin is that it is resistant to decay. It can hang around in soil or peat for thousands of years, even retarding the decay of other substances in the plant debris. It requires very specific organisms to break it down and, as lignin had only fairly recently evolved (around 420 million years ago), it is quite possible that these micro-organisms did not exist at the time. It is now thought that the accumulation of the coalfields in the Carboniferous period was due to this passing phase when no means of breaking down this lignin existed.

Making coal

As plant debris collects it begins to undergo biological, chemical and physical processes which drive off 'volatile' elements (hydrogen, nitrogen, oxygen and sulphur), turning the remains initially into peat and then into combustible coal. The proportion of carbon in the mass of material increases as coal is produced. Peat has less than 65 percent carbon. 'Lignite' (or 'brown coal') is a 'low rank' coal with 65 to 80 percent carbon; 'bituminous coal' has 80 to 91 percent and 'anthracite' over 91 percent. Bituminous and anthracite are 'mature' or 'high rank' coals, the former good for steam and/or coke-making and the latter for heating. In the Pennines, lower rank coal is found in the southern areas of the coalfields, with progressively higher ranking coal northwards.

The type of coal depends on the precise composition of the peat, the depth (and thus the pressure and temperature) to which it is buried and for how long. It is thought that there are two stages to the coal-making process. The first takes place near the surface, is mainly biological and produces lignite, while the second depends on chemical and physical effects and occurs at some considerable depth (in order to reach the required temperatures) over a sufficiently long period.

As it is buried the peat is compressed quite considerably, with 10 metres of peat being squeezed down to just about 1 metre of coal in rock form. It takes about 7,000 years for enough peat to accumulate to eventually produce a metre of coal, but it takes another eight million years of deep burial before the coal is created.

Despite the fact that the bulk of the thickness of the rocks of the Coal Measures is made up of shale and sandstone, because peat is compressed so much geologists still consider that the area was above ground for 95 percent of the time.

One terminological point is that the name bituminous coal came about because coal was thought to contain bitumen, but it does not. Bitumen is a general name for various viscous or solid mixtures of hydrocarbons which have lost their gaseous material. Natural bitumen can be seen seeping from a small limestone crag near Windy Knoll way outside the Coal Measures.

There are vast coalfields dating from the Carboniferous period on the continents of today, from the Americas to Eurasia. Fifty or more years ago, in the days before the theory of plate tectonics was accepted, it used to be argued that there must have been considerably more land in the Carboniferous period than there is now. This was the only way in which the widespread coal deposits (and the underlying Millstone Grit and Carboniferous Limestone strata) could be accounted for when the continents were treated as static, immovable objects. Similar contortions were needed to account for apparent oddities of the Carboniferous climate, which suggested that Britain experienced tropical conditions while equatorial regions suffered glaciation.

Today we can see that the movement of the continents, as proposed by the theory of plate tectonics, solves both conundrums. The coalfields were laid down when the continents were clustered near the equator. Since then they have split away from each other and been propelled to their present positions. The balance of continent and ocean was not so very different than it is today, nor was there some odd climate wobble. It is 'simply' that America and Eurasia have been driven by the earth's internal convection currents north from the equator on increasingly divergent paths. Not only is it accepted that the earth's surface is in constant motion, but so too are the ideas about the geological processes that created it.

The rocks of the Coal Measures are relatively less resistant than those of the underlying Millstone Grit. The result is that the relief in areas of the Coal Measures is fairly low. A good place to appreciate this is near Goldsitch farm (walk 11). On the footpaths near the farm the landscape is scattered with 'bell pits', the remnants of old coal diggings (photo 4.1). The area is flattish but framed with higher ground on either side, made up of the more resistant grits and sandstones of the Millstone Grit. Shale and even small lumps of coal can be found in the waste tips and crumbling shale can be seen in stream banks. Coal has been mined in these areas since the 15th century.

The rocks of the Coal Measures are sometimes reasonably abundant with plant fossils (and some freshwater animal fossils), but these come from the remains of soil from when the area was above water level for a while ('seat earth') and from the shale, rather than from the coal seams, where the plant matter was transformed (photo 4.4).

Photo 4.4

Plant fossil – a section of a branch pock-marked where leaves were directly attached to the branch. Coal Measures, South Wales. Width of view 80mm.

The end of the Carboniferous period is marked in the rocks by the virtual end of the appearance of coal seams in the present-day British Isles. By this time the chunk of continental plate that was to become the Peak District had moved roughly as far north of the equator as it had been to its south at the start of the Carboniferous period. During those 60 million years the continental plate had slowly moved northwards across the equator constantly accumulating rock – first platform, ramp and reef limestones of the Carboniferous Limestone, then the various sandstones and shale of the Millstone Grit and finally the mixed bag of the Coal Measures.

CHAPTER 5

Faulted and Folded

In the previous three chapters we have looked at the different environments in which our three great rock groups were laid down, seeing how the rock type depended on such conditions as rate of tectonic subsidence, cyclic changes in sea level and (in the case of both limestone and coal) the type of life form and what happened to it after death. We also saw how tectonic activity had other effects, such as spewing out lava and ash onto parts of the Carboniferous Limestone.

In this chapter we will look a little more closely at how tectonic forces lifted, tilted, folded and faulted the Pennine region during and immediately after the Carboniferous period, and how this is reflected in the scenery of the present day. During the Carboniferous period the world's continents were slowly coalescing into a single great continent: Pangaea. The generalised subsidence experienced by our area and the volcanic episodes were due to the interaction of these tectonic plates.

Towards the end of the Carboniferous period and for some 20 million years after it (during the 'Permian period'), continuing clashes of the coalescing plates had quite shattering effects to the south. These clashes also transmitted shudders through neighbouring areas causing large-scale deformation of the continental crust in what is now Belgium, northern France and southern Britain as well as more extensive effects in the 'Iberian-Armorican-Massif Central' region.

Our area lay just outside the most seriously affected zone but it was not wholly immune. The intensification of tectonic activity put an end to the prolonged subsidence which was such a constant feature through most of the Carboniferous period. The underlying tectonic plate was squeezed as the continents forced in on each other. Much of the pressure in the Pennines region was absorbed by earth movement on the line of ancient faults, and those areas which had fallen down to form basins when the crust was stretched now effectively popped back up along the same fault lines (with some crumpling and sideways displacement).

There was sufficient pressure applied to the tectonic plate to cause folding of the rocks forming the Pennine range. The overall pattern of folding is fairly complex, with different effects in different places. The ancient 'highs' (the tough granite under present-day South Yorkshire Dales and resistant rocks of the Wales-Brabant High of present-day White Peak) were the least affected by the folding, offering more resistance.

The all but horizontal bedding of the Carboniferous Limestone and Millstone Grit on such peaks as Penyghent, Ingleborough and Whernside in the South Yorkshire Dales is easy to observe.

Overall the limestone massif of the White Peak was subject to a bit more folding than the South Yorkshire Dales, but it is not easy to see as there are no handy peaks like those of the Dales to provide real world geological cross-sections of the strata. Generally the limestone exposed today in quarries and in railway and road cuttings shows either horizontal or slightly dipping beds; so you can see a tilt, but seldom an obvious upfold or downfold. To appreciate the change of dip it is necessary to take a fairly long linear walk through a slice of the landscape. This is possible in a few places such as the Wye Valley. You will need to observe the dip or tilt in different places and note how it changes. Following the Wye Valley the dips start from east to west, then it becomes flat and then changes again to dip to the east.

The underlying structure is of a gentle 'anticline', dipping steeply to the west and more gently to the east (diagram 5.1). The picture is actually a bit more complicated and the White Peak is often described as a 'dome' with gentle slopes running off in all directions from the high core. This is the main structure of the White Peak.

However, if the central parts of the area have put up a stout resistance to tectonic pressure, the clash of the tectonic plates and consequent mashing up and folding of the rocks are much more evident in peripheral parts of the Peak District than in its more central parts.

To the west of the White Peak, and most especially in the south-western corner, there is a series of fairly gentle synclines and anticlines. The best known is the Goyt syncline running from west of Kinder Scout down to the area between the Roaches and Ramshaw Rocks. The axis of the syncline is not horizontal, but dips to the north. This has brought the southern end of the syncline to the surface in this area. It is quite possible to see the syncline embedded in the scenery of the area (walk 11) from the way in which it interacts with the resistant and/or weak layers of sandstone and shale in the Millstone Grit and Coal Measures that crop out on the surface here.

The Roaches and Ramshaw Rocks are part of the syncline, displaying upturned bedding on an exposed scarp slope. Both the rocky edges have mightily impressive rock sculptures and both are part of the same sandstone bed, the Roaches Grit. This dips under the overlying 'saucer' to appear on both upturned edges (diagram 5.1 and photo 5.1).

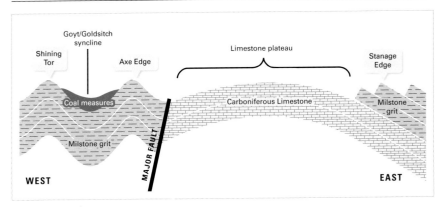

Diagram 5.1 | Simplified cross section through the White Peak.

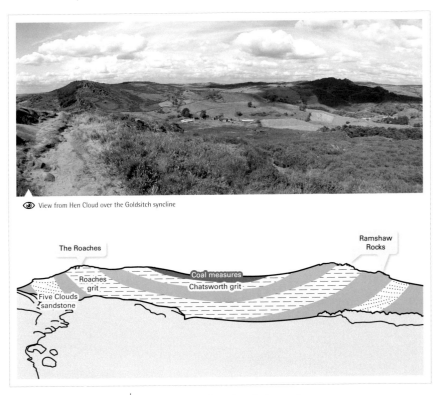

👁 View from Hen Cloud over the Goldsitch syncline

Diagram 5.2 + Photo 5.1 | The Roaches and Ramshaw Rocks syncline.

Here and in the Goyt Valley rocks of the Coal Measures are exposed at the surface. As has been mentioned in previous chapters, the rocks of the Coal Measures (mainly sandstones and shale with thin seams of coal and marine bands) are comparatively less resistant than the sandstones and grits (though with softer shale) of the Millstone Grit. This has resulted in low relief in the core of the syncline in both the Goyt Valley and the Gradbach/Goldsitch areas.

To the east and south-east of the Roaches/Gradbach area there are several anticlines and synclines: the Mixon-Morridge anticline; an unnamed syncline; the Ecton anticline; another unnamed syncline; and the western end of the main platform limestone anticline. The east-ernmost syncline can be seen from Narrowdale Hill (diagram 5.2 and photo 5.2) on walk 7. Here the river Manifold occupies the centre of the syncline and the upturned scarp slopes are easily visible, especially on the eastern limb overlooking the parallel Dove valley.

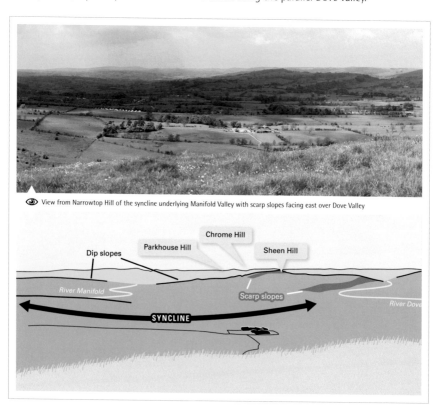

View from Narrowtop Hill of the syncline underlying Manifold Valley with scarp slopes facing east over Dove Valley

Diagram 5.3 + Photo 5.2 | The Manifold syncline

These are all large-scale earth structures; each wave measures several kilometres in length and is 4 or 5 kilometres wide. The folds are possible to detect only in wide perspective or by interpretation of geological maps. Not far from Narrowdale Hill, at the foot of the northern end of Ecton Hill, it is possible to see much sharper folds. These are most impressive at Apes Tor, in the Manifold valley (walk 7). Here some relatively less-resistant dark 'ramp limestone' (which has a high proportion of mineral matter) has been crushed as if in a vice between tougher rocks on either side – the main platform limestone on one side and the Millstone Grit on the other. This has resulted in some truly amazing small-scale folds.

The exposure of rocks at Apes Tor reveals a series of small, steep-limbed folds, with sharp anticlines and synclines replacing one another every 10 to 20 metres or so. Along the 150 metres or so of exposed rock face a whole series of such up-folds and down-folds can be seen one after the other (photos 5.3 and w7.5). Some of the folds are a bit hard to distinguish because of the presence of quite a bit of vegetation, but sufficient exposure exists for the folds to be clearly seen. Glimpses of rock exposure higher up the hillside show that the small, sharp folds exist there too.

Photo 5.3 |
Severe folding (syncline)
Apes Tor in impure,
dark, thinly-bedded,
ramp limestone.

There are smaller anticlines and synclines on the eastern margins of the limestone platform too. The 'Longstone Edge Anticline' (photo 5.4) in the north-east of the White Peak is unusual in that its axis runs east-west. It is significant that the crest of the anticline has been severely 'mineralised' with a dense zone of lead-bearing seams clustering along the axis of the anticline more or less parallel to its east-west bearing. Indeed, this area displays just about the densest area of mineral veins in the White Peak. The impressive scar created by the High Rake/Deep Rake open-cast workings follows one set of such veins. The workings on Longstone Edge itself are more traditional, with several disused shafts and workings.

Photo 5.4

Small-scale folding (anticline) on Longstone Edge in medium-bedded, shelf limestone.

There are a couple of anticlines in the south-east of the area as well. The Ashover Anticline and the Crich Anticline bring some limestone to the surface surrounded by Millstone Grit rocks. One point worth making is that when anticlines are created the upper layers of rock tend to be stretched and broken, allowing erosion to get to work relatively quickly. The result is that anticlines, or up-folds, counter-intuitively often tend to result in low relief. This is not always the case but certainly anticlines are more likely to reveal (or unpeel) older rocks. This is the case both with the main gentle anticline of the White Peak area as well as the Ashover/Crich anticlines.

The fickleness of geological phenomena can be seen in the Ashover and Crich exposures of the underlying limestone. The axis of the Ashover anticline is also the northwest-southeast course in the area of the present-day River Amber, illustrating the way in which erosion cuts down into the rocks exposed in an anticline (here exploiting a stratum of relatively weaker volcanic tuff). However, though both the axis of the anticline and the course of the river turn to a north-south direction just west of the exposure of the limestone, the river performs its change of direction some 4 kilometres further east of the axis of the anticline. Whereas the Ashover anticline is marked by a deep valley, the Crich section of the same anticline is marked by high ground where the limestone is exposed. This shows how the geology and the scenery interact, but not always in predictable ways.

It was during these tectonic contortions and stresses that metal mineral veins (which are such an important feature of the White Peak) were created when the residue of elements left over at the base of the crust at the end of the volcanic episodes shot up through any cracks or faults opened up during the earth movement.

Photo 5.5 | Odin Mine, below Mam Tor, just within the Carboniferous Limestone. The mine entrance (right) and a natural limestone cave (left) with shales upper right.

Photo 5.6 | A disused millstone used for crushing the mined ore.

Photo 5.7 | Old lead mine workings on a mineral rake or vein, Dove valley below Carder Low.

Photo 5.8 | Mineral workings, Dirtlow Rake.

Photo 5.9 | Galena (lead ore) (7cm wide).

Photo 5.10 | Fluorite or fluorspar (30mm long).

Mineralisation

In the Peak District, 'mineralisation' (the introduction of mineral veins including metals into rock) was the result of tectonic activity. Superheated fluids containing volatile elements were left over at the end of the volcanic eruptive episode. They circulated below the earth's crust under great pressure and rushed up any faults opened up during tectonic activity. They leached material from the surrounding rock as they rose to produce crystallised minerals, sometimes in the form of metal ores such as the lead ore, galena (photo 5.9).

Lead mining was a very important activity in the Peak District from the 15th to the 19th centuries, but is now defunct. The lead ore, galena, is found in veins or 'rakes' (small ones are known as 'scrims'). The line of old workings along a rake is usually pretty easy to spot (photos 5.7, 5.8, w5.1 and w7.4). The rakes are up to 10 metres wide and can be several kilometres long. Many of the longer rakes have names: Long Rake (about 8 kilometres in length), Great Rake and Dirtlow Rake to name just a few. They tend to concentrate in the western and northern parts of the White Peak, though rakes will be encountered in many other places.

The pits and hummocks that litter the line of the rakes are not the remains of a bit of quarrying just below the surface. Each pit is the surface expression of a mine shaft dug down through the vein. Just sufficient rock was left between the shafts to prevent a collapse. Lead was the most commonly mined metal, but considerable amounts of copper were dug out in the south-west of the area, for example on Ecton Hill (walk 7).

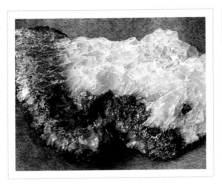

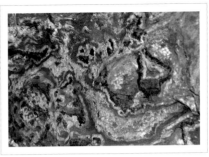

Photo 5.12 │ Blue John vein exposed in
Blue John Cavern (width of view is 0.75m).

Photo 5.11 │ Blue John (lump is 4cm long).

The Peak District is also the biggest source of 'fluorspar' (aka 'fluorite') in Britain. It is quarried for the fluorine it contains which is used in the manufacture of various fluorine-bearing chemicals. Some fluorspar is also used for flux in steel manufacture and similar industrial uses. About 40,000 tons of it are dug out of the hills of the Peaks each year (photo 5.10). A particular type of fluorspar (which has no industrial uses however) is the well-known coloured crystalline 'Blue John' stone used for jewellery and ornaments (photo 5.11).

Calcite, the crystal form of calcium carbonate, is frequently found throughout the White Peak in mineral rakes but also embedded within limestone rocks. It is mined and quarried for various industrial uses. Photo 5.13 shows a small piece of calcite embedded in limestone.

Another mineral, baryte, has various uses; one of these is to increase the density of drilling fluids in oil and gas exploration to minimise the chance of a 'blow-out'. Photo 5.14 shows a small lump of rock recovered from a waste tip on Ecton Hill. At first I saw the small ball shapes and thought it was a fossil. Looking at the sample under a hand lens, the little balls turned into some amazing clusters of plate-like structures. I couldn't find any similar fossils, but when reading up about baryte for this section I saw an example of the same plate-like clusters in a form known as 'cockscomb mass baryte'. The photograph shows an uncommon form of baryte, reminding us that minerals can appear in a multiplicity of forms. It is also a reminder that there are many interesting and unusual mineral, rock and fossil fragments to be found in old waste tips.

Photo 5.13 |
Calcite embedded
in limestone; calcite
piece is 2cm across.

Photo 5.14 |
Unusual form of
barite, known as
'cockscomb mass'
(width of view 2.5cm).

CHAPTER 6

Drainage Delights

In previous chapters we have looked at the creation of the Peak District's rocks. In this chapter and the next we look at their destruction. We will see how wind and chemical weathering have played a part in shaping the scenery, but mainly we will be looking at some of the consequences of the different ways in which water reacts with sandstone, shale and limestone. Topics such as 'drainage patterns' will seek to engage our attention. This may all sound rather dull, but it lies at the heart of the way in which the underlying rocks have been shaped in the present-day landscape.

We will skip the scores of millions of years between the end of the Carboniferous period to about 25 million years ago. Obviously this is a big leap to make. During that time, many more rocks were laid down on top of the Coal Measures (which covered the Millstone Grit which in turn covered the Carboniferous Limestone) and these rocks and others were eroded away.

We can take a slightly closer look at the period between 25 million years ago to just under 2 million years ago. Geologists believe that during this time the Peak District (and other highland areas in Britain) underwent progressive uplift due to tectonic pressures on the underlying continental plate. The uplift of the land would have led to the creation of new streams and, over time, a new drainage pattern emerged.

For most of this time the area was above sea level so most of the overlying rocks were removed from above the rocks of the Carboniferous period, thus exposing them on the surface. However, it is also thought that up to 150 metres of new rocks would have been laid down during the time when the sea level rose and inundated the land. These rocks have also been eroded away entirely in the Peak District.

At the start of the Ice Age, about 2.5 million years ago, we can envisage our area as a gently upwards-folded landscape with its own long-standing river systems that had carved courses down into the overlying rock strata. The last great Ice Age (for there have been many during those scores of millions of years since the Carboniferous Period rocks were laid down) took hold only very slowly, with a general cooling starting about that time. Actual glaciation within the Peak District area took hold about 700,000 years ago. There were cold and mild periods in the time since then with periods of intense glaciation and erosion by local glaciers and regional ice sheets. Much of the area was ice-free from perhaps as much as 100,000 years ago, although glacier ice last affected western parts of the Dark Peak about 20,000 years ago.

When the great ice sheets of the highlands of Britain and Ireland extended over the Peak District the rocks were intensely scoured and eroded, carving away softer rocks (shale and the Coal Measures most of all) leaving the undulating plateau that characterises both the Dark and the White Peak.

Even though most of the Peak District was free of ice for tens of thousands of years, until about 10,000 years ago the area was subject to intensely cold temperatures. A great deal of surface and some immediately sub-surface water would have been frozen for long periods. The surface water melted during summers or on warm winter days, so that it was repeatedly frozen and thawed. These are known as 'peri-glacial' conditions. As we will see, these cold times had many other effects, initiating many features of the present-day geology and scenery such as the dry valleys and cave systems, rocky edges, rock tors, scree slopes, landslides and 'river diversion'.

Peri-glacial conditions played an important role in shaping the rocky edges of the Dark Peak. Edges such as Curbar Edge, Stanage Edge and Hen Cloud, where the free face of the rocky scarp slope stands anywhere between 10 and 20 metres high, emerge out of a jumble of boulders and are increasingly covered by vegetation lower down the slope.

The rocky edge itself is chopped up into an irregular series of blocks and tors, often with deep gashes between them exposing a narrow gap between the rocks with a big drop below. The rocks are split on 'joints' (drying-out cracks created shortly after the rock was formed) which have been attacked by 'freeze-thaw' action where water gets into small crevices, expands on being frozen, then thaws again. Repeated time and again this process, aided by chemical weathering, starts to crack open the rocks. If the lower rocks are eroded away, the overhanging higher rocks will crumble and join the mass of boulders below (photo 6.1).

Eroded material moving down the scarp slope hides the surface of the dip slope and the steepness of the scarp slope, so it is necessary to try to imagine the edges with the veil of vegetation removed to appreciate the shape of the underlying landscape. This is easiest where quarrying has created great cliffs, for example in the quarries under Millstone Edge (photo 6.2). One particularly impressive example is natural, however, and can be seen when approaching Thorpe Cloud from below its west-facing scarp face (walk 11). First you have to walk up a long slope of vegetation, then up a steeper section of a mix of vegetation and

Photo 6.1 |
Undermining of overlying
beds on Stanage Edge.

Photo 6.2 |
Quarry face, Millstone Edge,
showing fuller extent of free
face on rocky edge. See
climber upper right for scale.

jumbled boulders as you near the face. Even with this skirt of material hiding the lower rock face, the looming crags above you are very impressive.

Water is not the only agent of erosion. Wind and chemical weathering also play a part. The two forces can be seen combined on many of the rocky edges of the Millstone Grit such as on Kinder Scout, Stanage Edge and the Roaches. Here the tracks expose grains of sand. This sand is produced by chemical weathering of certain types of sandstone (those with calcareous cement). On exposure to the atmosphere these sandstones undergo chemical reactions in the 'matrix' of tiny particles which cement the sand grains together into sandstone. As the cement is dissolved, the sand grains are released by the rock and fall to the ground. Here they

Photo 6.3
Bedding picked out
by wind, freeze/
thaw and chemical
erosion on boundaries
between sandstone
beds, Shining Tor.

await gales which whip up the sand and use it, literally, to sand-blast any exposed rock. The wind-driven sand grains erode the rock into the magnificent shapes we seen today on the rocky edges (photo 6.3).

We have seen how the stepped nature of the rocky edges, one scarp slope after another separated by a shallow dip slope, are the product of the interlaying of sandstone and shale. Another key feature of the Millstone Grit, the landslide (or landslip) is also a result of the interlayers of shale and grit. Over 600 landslides have been recorded by geomorphologists in the Peak District, the overwhelming majority of them in the Dark Peak. Many of the landslides were initiated by the ice which eroded steep-sided valleys into the uplands, leaving unstable slopes when the ice melted, but their underlying cause is the interplay of tough resistant sandstone and friable shale.

Although sandstone is a pretty tough rock and resistant to erosion; it is porous. Water can permeate through tiny pores between the sand grains in the 'solid' rock. However, the weak shale suddenly becomes tough when faced with water and presents an impermeable layer (except where broken by faults), so when the water permeating through sandstone

Photo 6.4 | Spring line on Nab End, Dove valley. Spring line is level with the farm building, left, at the boundary of sandstone (upper half of hill) and shale (lower half).

meets a layer of underlying shale it is unable to find a way further through the rock (unless there happens to be a fault to hand) and will follow the top of the shale to the surface where it comes out as springs, often forming a 'spring line' or line of springs.

On walks 5 and 6 such a spring line can be discerned on the western side of the Dove valley some way up from the river itself at the boundary between the sandstone (which forms the high points above the river to the west) and the shale (which underlies the lower part of the valley on both sides). This is where the valley side becomes less steep as the resistant sandstone has produced a steeper slope and the shale a gentle drop to the stream. The springs themselves are not easy to spot, but their position is betrayed by the fact that farms on that side of the valley are located at roughly the same height, on the spring line. On walk 5, from Parkhouse Hill especially, it is actually possible to see where stream gullies emerge on the northern point of Nab End (photo 6.4). There is also a spring line on the eastern side of the valley at the junction of the Millstone Grit shale with the Carboniferous Limestone (chapter 7).

The water on the top of the shale and at the bottom of sandstone beds comes under great pressure ('pore pressure') when the sandstone is very wet and saturated with water. The water on top of the shale can then act as lubrication for landslides where the slopes are oversteepened (as many were at the end of the ice age). The tendency of shale to erode and leave overhanging sandstone ensures that steep slopes are unstable. These elements combine to create landslides where the lower layer of shale deforms, causing a collapse or slide.

There are various different types of landslide. In some cases, such as in Bretton Clough (walk 2, photos w2.2, w2.3 and w2.4), whole massive blocks of the hillside, have clearly slidden over a collapsed lower layer, moving some distance downhill without collapsing into a jumbled mass. Walking within the landslide area is a fascinating experience as the slipped blocks tower around you like isolated knolls.

Other landslides are deeper, rotational slides and the slipped mass has more or less lost its coherence. The most famous of the Peak District's landslides is on the eastern face of Mam Tor (see below), not least because it provides a sharp lesson in the limits of human ability to tame geological processes. Here the sandstone rocks have broken up into boulders while the shale has been smashed up and now flows downwards so the lower part of the landslide is still in motion. Repeated attempts to keep a road open through this area were finally abandoned in 1979 after around 100 years of efforts to keep it passable. The road actually provides a useful illustration of the continuing slide as the road seems to be stretching and flowing before your very eyes (photo 6.5).

Photo 6.5 | Mam Tor landslip – lower section with crushed shale sliding slowly downhill taking the road with it.

The Mam Tor landslip

The last traces of glacial ice in this area around Mam Tor disappeared about 80,000 years ago. However, it remained intensely cold until around about 10,000 years ago. Under such conditions the rocks were subject to constant freezing of any water in cracks and surface pores forcing expansion, followed by thawing and eventual break-down of the mechanical strength or coherence of the rock. Many of the landslides in the Pennine range were sparked off during those long years of repeated freeze-thaw.

The Mam Tor landslide is thought to be about 3,500–4,000 years old, somewhat more recent than the landslides on the northern flank of the ridge, such as the Back

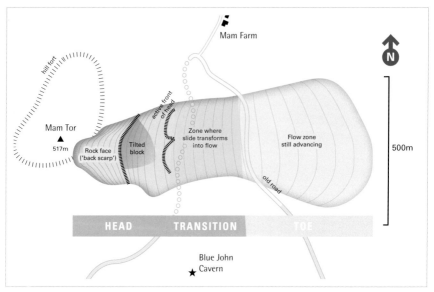

Diagram 6.1 | Zones of activity in the Mam Tor landslip.

Tor landslide which probably occurred about 8,000 years ago. These older landslides in the northern flanks of the ridge are now largely inactive (except for falling blocks). The Mam Tor landslide, however, is still on the move; its front creeps forward an average of 10 centimetres a year (more in wet years, less in dry ones).

The Mam Tor Beds which make up the body of Mam Tor are formed by a repeated cycle of a 'massive' sandstone, a bedded sandstone, a bedded siltstone, shale and finally a mudstone. This is a classic example of what geologists call a 'turbidite' sedimentary sequence, typical of a storm or earthquake-generated sudden flow of sediments off the end of a delta. The heavier sediments settle first, then slowly grading ever smaller in size. Each cycle represents another earthquake or storm.

The rocks at the base of Mam Tor (and indeed underlying the Hope valley) are shales, known as the Edale Shales. These weak rocks have been severely crumpled by the tectonic forces. The more resistant limestones to the south and sandstones of the Millstone Grit (including the Mam Tor Beds) to the west and north have withstood the great pressures, being only gently folded. However the Edale Shales have been severely mashed up and are particularly vulnerable to chemical weathering when exposed to the atmosphere. This further weakens the rock's physical strength and it is easily eroded away at the surface.

The Edale Shales thus provided very weak foundations; eventually they foundered, bringing the overlying rocks crashing down to create a mix of sandstone boulders and shale fragments.

Among the mass of fallen rocks the sandstones retain their coherence as boulders, but the shales break up physically and chemically into a mass of fragments. The pressure of the upslope fragments causes the lower fragments to flow downhill, especially when lubricated by plenty of rainfall. The angle of the hummocky landslide mass is on average 12 degrees. It is estimated that the angle will need to fall to below 11 degrees before the landslide becomes stable, and that this will take another 4,000 years.

The main collapse has taken place, but erosion on a small scale still causes individual lumps of rock and even boulders to come crashing down at unpredictable intervals. The mountain's nickname, the Shivering Mountain, is derived from its habit of shedding rock and reminds us that it is dangerous to go too close to the exposed rocks.

Immediately below the great rock face, which is 80 metres high, are mounds of boulders and vegetation. This area is somewhat safer, but keep well away from the rock face nonetheless.

Continued movement of the lower section of hummocks is most evident when looking at the section of the closed road from the north. The road was built in 1810 and was repaired time and again until it was finally abandoned in 1979. It is a useful marker showing just how the material is slipping at different rates in different places. In one spot the road has slid down by several metres.

The section of the landslide mass within the sections of the road above and below the hairpin bend is the 'transition' zone between the higher stable blocks and the creeping shale mass with spring lines, pools of water and mineral staining.

So far the toe of landslide mass has extended forward by some 750 metres. It is still slowly pushing forward and tilting fences, barns, electricity poles and trees before eventually engulfing them.

Photo 6.6

Landslip on the northern
flank of Rushup Edge,
seen from the path to
Mam Nick from the
summit of Mam Tor.

The Mam Tor is only one of several landslides on the Lose Hill/Mam Tor/Rushup Edge ridge (photo 6.6, also walk 3, photos w3.3 and w3.4). The slide underneath Back Tor on the north side of the ridge is a miniature version of the Mam Tor landslide, with a small-scale steep rock face with layered sandstone and shale (it lacks only an abandoned miniature road). It is a complex rotational slide that has created a hollowed area beneath the rock collapse face. The area affected by the landslide covers some 60 hectares and stretches right down the hillside as hummocky ground.

On the walk down from the summit of Back Tor heading towards Mam Tor there is an excellent example of highly weathered shale with resistant sandstone, increasingly insecure, jutting out above. It's almost as if a geography teacher had put it there for the purpose of easily enlightening the pupils, 'Oh look, here's one I made earlier' (photo 3.4).

A landslide on the north-east end of Lose Hill is thought to have occurred about 2,500 to 3,500 years ago, while those in the Alport valley further north date from as far back as 8,000 years ago. The more the slope was oversteepened, the more rapidly that erosion would have its dramatic effect.

One of the most dramatic examples of a landslide is one that never fulfilled its potential. Lud's Church (about 2 kilometres north of the Roaches in Forest Wood near Gradbach) is now well hidden in woodland, but is part of an area which has seen quite a substantial landslide. Lud's Church itself is a deep, twisting gash up to 3 metres wide at the top of the slide where the rock on the downhill side has torn away from the main rock face on the uphill side but has not crashed downhill along with other material from the landslide; a hummocky terrain (not easily discerned beneath the tree cover, photo w11.5) has been formed. The walk through the gash (walk 11) is highly atmospheric and instructive about forces involved in landslides.

CHAPTER 7

Solution and Superimposition

Limestone is a very tough rock; it is one that cuts the flesh of climbers more easily than most rocks. It is 'mechanically strong', often forming vertical or even overhanging cliffs in natural gorges and non-natural quarries. In rain water it is simply dissolved away, however.

Calcium carbonate is dissolved by a weak acid, for example rain water, which can also extract carbon dioxide from soil while it filters through to the rock to add to its dissolving power. The calcium carbonate becomes the soluble calcium bicarbonate and is carried away in drainage water. This results in some very special characteristics of limestone landscapes, such as sink holes and caverns as well as unique features such as stalagmites, stalactites and other forms of re-precipitated calcium carbonate, that is, when its dissolved form is precipitated back out of water to its solid form.

One consequence of this is that limestone does not produce a soil in the same way as other rocks do because it is dissolved and washed away. This means that the soil we see today in the White Peak has been blown in from other areas. Where the wind has failed to bring in sufficient matter to make a soil we get bare limestone, known as 'limestone pavement' (though some geomorphologists and botanists suggest that natural soil cover was lost as a result of deforestation). There are only a few very small patches of limestone pavement in the Peak District (although there are impressive spreads in the South Yorkshire Dales and, most spectacularly, in the Burren region of western Ireland). A small section of limestone pavement can be seen on Carder Low on walk 6 (photos 7.1 and 7.2 overleaf).

Limestone pavements would not be very popular if proffered by a local council as an urban pavement, but are a much-loved feature of limestone; they helpfully show us the structure of internal weaknesses where carbon-rich water can dissolve a channel into the limestone. The slabs of limestone called 'grykes' (or 'grikes') are separated by irregular vertical gaps called 'clints'. The clints are drying joints formed early in the rock's life. When exposed at the surface, the joints are widened into fissures (gaps that threaten to trip the unwary walker). Blown-in soil and plant matter will also collect in these clints, enriching rain water with additional carbon dioxide from the breakdown of plant matter. The joints are opened up deeper and deeper and turned into underground water channels which swallow up any surface water.

Photo 7.1 | Limestone pavement at Carder Low.

Photo 7.2 | Gleninagh Mountain, Burren, County Galway, western Ireland.

The sink hole (or swallow hole, swallet, shake hole or pot hole) is one of the most enthralling of the features of limestone. They frequently occur on the junction between Millstone Grit and Carboniferous Limestone, and take various forms. One is where the land collapses above a widening underground channel. At Stanley Moor near Buxton, where there is a group of sink holes, there are two which are 10 metres deep (042 714). In other cases, such as at Windy Knoll (photo 7.3) or Little Bull Pit, the stream runs into a cave.

Photo 7.3 |
Cave entrance,
Windy Knoll.

On the junction between the shales of the Millstone Grit and the mainly reef limestones of the Carboniferous Limestone on the southern edge of the Mam Tor and Rushup Edge ridge, there is a run of several sink holes where the surface rain water drains off the shale at the bottom of the ridge onto the limestone and immediately disappears into holes in the ground. The series of sink holes starts just below Mam Tor (near the junction of the closed road with the main road at 1285 8312) where there is an undistinguished hole in the ground; the Mam Tor Swallow hole (photo 7.4). The nearby cave at Windy Knoll (near a rock face which naturally oozes bitumen, photo 7.5) is another in the series, as is Giant's Hole and several others running in a line to the south-west, including the 'pot holes' marked on the OS map at 1080 8180 and 1020 8155. The Bull Pit at 1065 8140 is up to 50 metres in diameter and 50 metres deep with steeply sloping walls. At the Little Bull Pit, the stream enters a cave 3 metres high at the base of some limestone crags.

Photo 7.4 | Mam Tor sink hole on the boundary between the Millstone Grit (top) and Carboniferous Limestone (bottom).

Photo 7.5 | Natural bitumen oozing out of the limestone from a crag just to the right of Windy Knoll cave.

One of the potentially most impressive examples of such disappearing streams is at Waterfall Swallet (199 771). Here a stream draining off the Millstone Grit of Eyam Edge falls over a 10 metre high crag, forming a waterfall draining into a large curved hole about 20 metres round, with sheer walls on three sides and a more gentle rise on the fourth side (photo 7.6). The water crosses the floor of the hole and disappears underground into a small hole. Unfortunately this prize example of a large sink hole is virtually invisible and hard to get close to thanks to dense vegetation; indeed, in summer it may even be impossible to find. There is no nearby footpath so it is a bit off-track when walking and there is limited parking. Access is 'informal' and presumably discouraged by neglect but, if passing, it may be worth a diversion (especially in wet weather or in winter). In any other district of the Pennines, or Britain for that matter, this would be a prime geological feature.

Photo 7.6

Waterfall Swallet.

To find the swallet, walk down the rough vehicle track to the immediate left (west) of the entrance track to the caravan site on the minor road about 1.5 kilometres west of Eyam. Look out for a minor path to the left after about 10 metres from the road (and well before the rough vehicle track bears sharp left). The minor path, if you can find it, cuts through thick vegetation and takes you down the gentle slope. Be extremely careful if you approach the edge of the hole from any other direction, as there are sheer drops of up to 10 metres. You can watch a clip of the path of the stream online at youtu.be/ksTsmtCOE8c (though it was taken in dry weather so the waterfall is unimpressive).

Some sink holes are naturally unimpressive. A few kilometres from Waterfall Swallet, just below the village of Eyam deep in the wooded Eyam Delf (below the rock tor 'Cucklet Church' which is thought to be a collapsed and now exposed cavern, photo 7.7), is a remarkably unexciting sink hole (photo 7.8). It is literally just a small, dirty hole in the soil surrounded by a fence. Nonetheless, however small and insignificant the sink hole, it could lead to a significant underground cave system. The cave system under Eyam Delf is claimed to be one of the oldest in the White Peak, but is only one of many.

Photo 7.7 | 'Cucklet Church', an old underground cavern, now exposed on the surface in Eyam Delf.

Photo 7.8 | Inconspicuous sink hole, Eyam Delf.

Once underground, the acidic water cuts channels which get bigger and bigger so that caverns are opened up lower and lower in the limestone until the water table is met. Stalactites (hanging from the roof of a cavern) and stalagmites (building up from the cavern floor) are a much-loved feature of caves and caverns (photo 7.9). They are made of the dissolved calcium carbonate, which is held in solution in water as calcium bicarbonate before re-precipitating out as the water drips down and through the limestone. The excess carbon dioxide in the water diffuses into the cave air when the water is exposed to it.

Photo 7.9 |
Slender stalactites and a handful of stumpy stalagmites, Treak Cavern.

The amounts of calcium carbonate re-precipitated by each drop of water are absolutely tiny but can build up over many thousands of years to create these strange candle-like features. Stalactites are hollow pipes, while stalagmites are solid. Unfortunately these features were popular trophies in the early days of cave exploration, geological study and tourism and many were ripped out of the caves presently open to the public leaving largely impoverished displays today.

Photo 7.10 |

Calcium carbonate solid 'waterfall', Blue John Cavern.

Calcium carbonate can also precipitate out to form curtain shapes on the walls of caverns that look like frozen, coloured waterfalls (photo 7.10). Where water rich in calcium bicarbonate emerges from underground onto the surface at springs, it can produce a rock known as 'tufa' from re-precipitating the calcium carbonate onto a surface feature.

That brings us back from the subterranean to the surface, because if rainwater goes underground at one point, it is likely to come back out somewhere lower down. There are two basic places where this can happen: first on reaching the 'water table', that is, the surface at which porous rocks become saturated and second on reaching impermeable rocks such as shale or volcanic rocks. Often this happens on a spring line (the antithesis to the line of sink holes). Frequently, the location of the spring line can be detected by the presence of farm houses which were located close to the springs.

As mentioned in the previous chapter, the River Dove between Nab End and Hartington has cut its course into shale, with sandstone on the west side of the valley and limestone on the east side. Both these rocks are permeable (though in different ways) while shale is not and a spring line is found on both sides of the valley throughout its length in this section. Walk 11 partly follows the eastern spring line at Meadow Farm, Underhill Farm and Glutton Bridge.

Elsewhere the location of springs can be less regular and much more contingent. Walk 15 passes a couple of examples where springs result from the presence of impermeable volcanic rocks in the middle of limestone beds. In one case (at the foot of Chelmorton Low) a spring occurs where some faults have pushed some volcanic rocks forward, juxtaposing the two rock types (limestone and lava) out of line with most of the area. In the other case (in Chee Dale) it occurs where the volcanic rocks are exposed in the floor of the valley.

Elsewhere streams or rivers emerge from caves. Lathkill Dale cave (walk 12) is a good example. Here an underground stream usually burbles forth, emerging to convert the dry valley of its upper reaches into a standard river-bearing one. In dry weather, however, nothing emerges from the cave entrance (photo w12.4). The stream then emerges lower down the valley at one point or another, lined as it is with springs. Lathkill Dale is dry from its head to whichever point the stream emerges, but in the Manifold valley the river rises and initially flows over the Millstone Grit on the surface as a standard river. It only disappears shortly after it crosses into the Carboniferous Limestone, emerging again lower down (though in wet weather it abjures the disappearing trick).

Interestingly, the steep-sided, almost gorge-like, dry valley section of Lathkill Dale around Ricklow Quarry is unusual as most of the gorges and near-gorges (such as Chee Dale and Dovedale) do have a surface river. However, the dry valley at the start of Lathkill Dale (known as Bagshaw Dale) is a classic feature of the Carboniferous Limestone. It is gentle-sided and grassy, typical of dozens of similar waterless valleys of the White Peak. Cave Dale (walk 13) is a classic dry valley in its upper section in the 'shelf limestone' (photo 7.11).

Photo 7.11

Dry valley, Cave Dale.

These dry valleys were clearly created by rivers in the same way as other ordinary water carrying valleys, but now run dry all the time. How can this be explained? It used to be popular to look on dry valleys and gorges as caverns where the roof has collapsed. The current theory is that they must have been cut by water at a time when the water table was higher than it is now. When it dropped, the streams were able to sink into the limestone and drain away underground until meeting the lowered water table or impermeable rocks. The lowering of the water table is attributed to tectonic 'uplift' of the land. An alternative view is that frozen ground water during peri-glacial conditions had the same effect. It may be that both factors contributed.

Glaciation is also thought to have been responsible for diverting some of the pre-glacial rivers into a new drainage pattern at the end of the Ice Age. The general idea of glacial forces changing the course of rivers is well established (outside our area, the Thames, for example, was diverted onto its present course from its previous one to the north of the Chilterns). The problem comes, in our area, when trying to determine whether some 'discordant' feature of a present-day river is due to glaciation or some other factor (or a combination).

A common discordant feature of the Carboniferous Limestone (and one which occurs to a lesser extent in the Millstone Grit) is known to geologists as 'superimposed drainage'. Glaciation may be one factor behind this phenomenon, but there are others too.

One noticeable feature of the river systems in the White Peak is the way that rivers have cut deep valleys or gorges all the way through the limestone. The Wye rises west of Buxton and yet it flows east through higher land to reach the Millstone Grit east of the limestone, where it joins the south-flowing Derwent. The gorge cut by the Wye at Chee Tor is the most impressive gorge in the Peak District (photo 7.12, w15.2, w15.3 and w15.4) and indicates the amount of work needed by the river to cut its course into the limestone (walk 15). The Derwent's early course is south and then it flows south-east along the boundary between the Carboniferous Limestone and the Millstone Grit. Near Matlock it does a sharp swerve to the south, avoiding the easy course to the south-east, to cut a steep-sided gorge through the limestone (the gorge is seen from viewpoints on walk 14).

Similarly, the River Dove is channelled along the boundary between the Carboniferous Limestone and the Millstone Grit in its central section (between Chrome Hill and Hartington, walks 5 and 6) then ignores the low land to the west and cuts a much longer and narrower gorge through the highland of the limestone (photos 7.13 and w8.2). These are all examples of superimposed drainage as the natural course would have been to avoid the intervening higher land and the need to cut deep gorges.

Photo 7.12 |
Climbers on the
overhanging walls
of the limestone
gorge at Chee Tor.

Photo 7.13 |
Superimposed drainage
in Dovedale cuts a
narrow gorge into
knoll reef limestone.

The explanation for this phenomenon is that the river's course was determined many years ago, but since then masses of overlying rocks have been eroded away. The river has maintained the old river course, cutting down into the underlying rock, resulting in a deep-sided valley or even a gorge. An alternative theory is that the land has undergone very slow uplift, slow enough for the river to erode the rocks and keep its existing course. However, this second explanation seems to demand a longer timescale over which it is unlikely that the rivers could have maintained a course.

It is interesting to note that all the rivers that flow through the limestone on the surface either rise outside the limestone or are tributaries of such rivers (so that, for example, the Lathkill Dale river is a tributary of the Derwent).

Superimposed drainage is a very common feature of White Peak drainage, but it can also affect the Millstone Grit which offers examples of where streams ignore the obvious course through soft shale and instead swing away to cut a deep channel through tough sandstone. This is well illustrated on walk 4 at the head of the River Manifold and the River Dove – both of which cut steep-sided and apparently unnecessary channels through the sandstone. Another example is seen on walk 11 where a stream cuts across the notoriously tough sandstone known as the Chatsworth Grit near the Roaches (which also forms the well-known edges of Stanage Edge and Curbar Edge). However, in this case, some suggestions have been made that glacial diversion of Black Brook is responsible. The current theory is that sub-glacial meltwater streams (which are very powerful) carved out meltwater channels which became incorporated into the post-glacial drainage pattern. Drainage, on the surface or underground, is both a product and an agent of the geology and scenery, adding scenic delight and interest to the landscape.

CHAPTER 8

Peak and People

The post-glacial environment brought about many changes: the development of soil and vegetation cover, forestation, the initiation and/or reactivation of landslides, the formation of modern flood plains, the formation of peat, the establishment of the drainage system, extension of the drying out of limestone valleys and the deepening of cave systems. Another influence began to play an increasingly important role ... human beings.

The first dramatic intervention by humans was progressive deforestation leading to the erosion of the soil and peat. About 5,000 years ago the Millstone Grit moorlands in the eastern part of the Peak District supported an oak and alder dominated forest, broken only on the exposed rocky edges. After that time forest cover was rapidly reduced as farming was introduced which led to more and more land clearances (mainly for pasture). It was a revolutionary change which deeply affected the natural landscape. The removal of tree cover in the Dark Peak led to the formation of today's peat bogs.

Today the main reminders of these early inhabitants in the Dark Peak are the many prehistoric monuments, such as on Eyam Moor. But it was the better soil of the limestone that attracted most interest in those times. The White Peak is littered with chambered tombs, burial mounds and cairns. It also features two important prehistoric henge or ring monument sites: Arbor Low (walk 12) and the 'Bull Ring' henge north of Buxton near the quarrying village of Dove Holes (which is nowhere near the Dove Holes caves in Dovedale).

Photo 8.1
Dene Quarry, Dean
Hollow, Middleton; a
modern limestone quarry.

Mining and quarrying in the Peak District began on a small scale in those early days of human settlement and exploitation. The lines of mineral rakes with their pits and mounds and smaller abandoned limestone quarries are signs of later exploitation, most especially in the 19th century. Massive quarries dug into the limestone are found all over the White Peak today – the six biggest sites each hack out of the ground in excess of 1 million tons of material every year (photo 8.1).

Little is known about early mining and quarrying, but by the 17th century there were probably 4,000 lead workers employed in the area with another 20,000 or more dependents. The industry thus directly supported about one-third of the total population of Derbyshire. The area would have been alive with limestone burning, coal mining, 'marble' quarrying, grindstone quarrying and millstone quarrying. By the late 17th century, millstones were being exported from the Peaks all over Britain and even to the continent (photo 8.2).

Photo 8.2

Half-completed and abandoned millstone, Baslow Edge.

By the end of the 17th century the White Peak had developed into one of the cradles of the Industrial Revolution. Water-powered mills ushered in the greatest change in human society since the advent of farming. Derby's silk mill opened in 1719 and Arkwright's first cotton mill, at Cromford, in 1771. Further north the fast-flowing streams were used to power mills for grinding and sharpening as well as for powering textile-making machines.

At the same time educated people were beginning to take an interest in the highlands of Britain. The Peak District was the first British wilderness to be 'discovered', well before the mountains of Wales, the Lakes and Scotland. This discovery was made before the Romantics had written a new script for appraising highland landscapes. There was attraction to the rough scenery, but it was expressed as an attraction to ugliness. The local poet and writer Charles Cotton (after whom a pub is named in Hartington) viewed his surrounds as one of 'impostuous boils' and 'the warts and pudenda of nature'. To William Stukeley the Peaks were the 'British Alps' and Cratcliffe Tor was 'a monstrous parcel of gigantic rocks, seemingly pil'd one a top of another as in the war of the gods'. Daniel Defoe considered it 'a howling wilderness', 'perhaps the most desolate, wild and abandoned country in all England'.

Attitudes changed and more and more people recognised beauty in the wilderness. Dovedale became the most illustrious of the area's natural attractions. For Wordsworth it was expressed as 'Dovedale's dreamy spires' (a reference to Tissington Spires, a rock tor in Dovedale (walk 8). Several tors (in Dovedale, Matlock Dale, Middleton Dale and near Buxton) were named Lover's Leap, each with its own little legend to account for the name. There was an increase in demand for books and illustrations. Turner and other painters came and portrayed the scenery in their own ways. During the French and Napoleonic Wars, the British upper classes were denied access to the continent and their usual Grand Tours. The White Peak increasingly became a substitute for jaunts into the wild. Increasing numbers came to peer into the Devil's Arse (how today's Peak Cavern was long known). Even when the legend that wind rushed through the cavern to be expelled from its orifice was disproved it remained a popular attraction, not least for rogues and vagabonds.

Turnpike roads were built which increasingly opened up the countryside to ever more visitors. Buxton and the Matlocks (Matlock Bath, Matlock Dale, Matlock Bridge, Matlock Green and Old Matlock or Matlock Town) developed into tourist bath towns and attracted visitors as an alternative to Bath itself. More and more walkers visited the area, advised by guidebooks specially written for walkers. Dr William Kitchiner's 1825 title gives a hint of the genre: *Traveller's Oracle: or Maxims for Locomotion, containing Precepts for Promoting the Pleasures and Hints for Preserving the Health of Travellers.*

Antiquarians, 'scientists' and 'geologists' began to explore the area in more detail and to publish books and papers about the area's natural history (while ripping irreplaceable stalagmites and stalactites out of limestone caverns). Sometimes they were confused (as at times we can be today) about whether a particular feature was natural or artificial and many an explanation they devised would get short shrift today. However, along with collectors of fossils and minerals, they opened up the way for long-term scientific study which continues today revealing ever more about the forces that created the landscape.

One example was John Hutchison's book published in 1809, entitled *Tour through the High Peak of Derbyshire, including an account of the natural and subterranean curiosities of that country; the beautiful crystallised cavern lately discovered at Bradwell; and the romantic scenery of the Woodlands, never before described.*

But it was not all natural beauty. No doubt there were far fewer people walking the valleys and lows then than the great crowds encountered today (and there were few proper paths). Yet that did not mean that the vales could be enjoyed in peace and solitude. One writer (Gilpin) described Middleton Dale as 'a defile between jagged rock precipices, whose drama was heightened by the explosions in its quarries and the palls of smoke and dust created by the limestone burners'.

The jagged contrast between the beauty of nature and ugly human endeavour appalled early environmentalists. As early as 1790 John Byng thundered that 'speaking as a tourist, these vales have lost all their beauties; the rural cot has given place to the lofty red mill, and the grand house of the overseers ... Every rural sound is sunk in the clamours of the cotton works'. Nearly a century later, after the coming of the railway and many more visitors, Ruskin exclaimed about the Wye Valley that 'you entertained a Railroad through the valley – you blasted its rocks away, heaped thousands of tons of shale into its lovely stream. The valley is gone, and the Gods with it; and now every fool in Buxton can be at Bakewell in half-an-hour, and every fool in Bakewell in Buxton'.

Ironically, it was the writings of Ruskin and others that drew the visitors by describing the natural beauty and encouraging readers to get out and taste it for themselves. One Manchester educationalist, James Croston, recommended walking in 1860 for 'combining recreation with intellectual amusement, and to cultivate a more close acquaintance with the charms of nature'. James Blatchford, journalist and socialist, was 'urging city dwellers to enjoy and reclaim the countryside'.

Photo 8.3

Railways dug into the heart of the Peaks brought noise, steam, industry and visitors. Now many are delightful trails through the geology and scenery. Rock outcrops on either side of the cutting are dolomite, Hopton Tunnel.

Early tourism had been largely restricted to the White Peak, but as rambling became more popular the adventurous began to explore the Dark Peak. One early nineteenth century pioneer who ventured into this previously 'untrodden district' encountered 'groughs above twenty feet wide whose storm-laden peat often sucked them in to their thighs' so that they arrived at their destination, 'drenched with rain, dropping with sweat and covered with dirt'.

As cycling became popular cyclists added to the numbers of visitors. By 1924 there were 24 walking and field clubs in Sheffield and 38 in Manchester. They organised walks and activities, but also campaigned to protect rights of way and for wider access. In the inter-war period, battles over closed footpaths were common. On one occasion eight council staff, supported by 200 ramblers, took pickaxes and other tools to unblock illegally closed paths. By the 1930s the restrictions on access led to the 'mass trepass' actions at Winnats and Kinder Scout.

Not all problems of access have been solved. In researching the walks in this book, I twice had to lie on the ground and shuffle forwards to pass under an electric fence. Though it was dusty and dirty, it wasn't wet on either occasion so I suppose I should be grateful. Once I tried to follow a route through access land, but discovered that there was no means of access to the access land, it being made securely inaccessible by stone walls and barbed wire fences.

Photo 8.4

Peat and people – a lost sole in the Dark Peak's untamed wildness.

Public access is immeasurably better compared with less than a century ago. There is little or nothing to stop the walker seeking out beautiful landscapes and fascinating geological features on the dense network of public footpaths and the newly available access land. I hope that this book adds a little interest to the walks of those who do venture out into this wonderful landscape.

About the Walks

Two factors have been central to selecting the walks the quality of views and geological/ geomorphological interest. They are rather different from the walks (or more usually drives) in many geology guides which concentrate on certain locations and look intensely at the rocks. The primary purpose of this book is to enable the reader to enjoy a good walk. The stuff about the geology is intended to enhance the walk.

The walks are of various lengths and levels of toughness, from a pretty easy short walk to long, tough ones. They are designed with the average hillwalker in mind and often take the reader up and down the valley sides and hills of the area. You may choose to make a detour around my instructions to 'go up the steep slope'.

The sketch maps for the walks are designed to show the general route and are for use in conjunction with the OS 1:25,000 map, OL1 and OL24 (these are both excellent maps covering a vast area and are very good value; they are a must for any walker). The sketch maps are very emphatically not designed to be sufficient to use on their own as it is impossible to show the precise route with sufficient accuracy. It is thus essential, to plan the route on the map before going out and to take the map for use when out walking. Grid references are given as six or eight figures as appropriate; many have been verified using GPS.

It will make sense to read the walk description before going on the walk and then to take a photocopy of the relevant pages, or the book itself, along on the walk as a reminder of what to see and where.

I have borrowed (and slightly adapted) a system for ranking the challenges of each walk from Ralph Storer's book, *100 Best Routes on Scottish Mountains*. This system allows a more nuanced assessment to be given than a vague 'hard' or 'easy'. For each walk I give a ranking on a scale of 1 to 5 (1 – easiest, 5 – hardest) for three areas: navigation, terrain and overall seriousness. Even so some arbitrariness must apply. For example, a walk may generally be very easy navigation or terrain-wise, but still have one or two short but seriously more challenging sections. In such situations I have given the ranking earned by the most difficult section.

A high navigation ranking means that there are places or sections on the route where it would be easy to make an error and head off in the wrong direction. Difficulties in intricate navigation through fields and footpaths near to farms and settlements don't merit a high rating; this sort of navigational problem shouldn't lead to a serious problem that needs the mountain rescue to be called out!

A high score for terrain may be due to either sections of steep ground or some very rough going (usually tussocky grass/heather and hidden boulders and holes in the ground).

By overall seriousness, I mean the chance for things to go badly wrong in the event of a minor navigation error or a simple accident; in general, the most 'serious' walks are those that go up onto the moorlands.

All the rankings apply to good weather conditions with clear views of the walk. I must recommend that you do not attempt any of the higher level walks in tempestuous weather.

I have used some terms in specific ways. In general I have used the term 'track' for any obvious trail on the ground, from a motor-vehicle track to a sheep track and anything in between. Some tracks are marked on the 1:25,000 OS map by thin dashed black line, but many more are not marked at all. Terms such as narrow track, wispy track and twisting track are all, I hope, self-explanatory. By 'footpath' I mean a public right of way marked in green on the OS 1:25,000 map (thus including bridleways). Note that the course of the actual track on the ground may not be the same as the line of the footpath shown in green on the map; this can be confusing if navigating in an unfamiliar area so watch out.

Getting to the walks

The walks have been arranged to start/finish near to bus routes or stops (or train stations). The only exceptions are walk 7 (Wolfscote Dale), walk 11 (the Roaches) and walk 14 (National Stone Centre and Middleton). These walks can be slightly re-arranged to use public transport. Walk 7 can be started and finished at Hartington; walk 11 can be started/finished at Ramshaw Rocks and walk 14 can be started/finished at Wirksworth.

There is a website at www.peakdistrict.gov.uk/index/visiting/publictransport.htm which promises much but delivers very little. When I tried to use it I found the online journey planner link to be broken. Also the 'interactive map' required me to endure a page asking me to accept conditions of use, before presenting me with a simple large scale (and therefore useless) map and then an empty screen saying nothing more than 'Derbyshire Partnerships'. The only link which did work was one where you can order online a bus timetable for the price of £1.50. That may be useful, but not a lot. Why, in modern times, can they not get it together to post a simple online timetable (as other National Parks/Counties do) instead of over-ambitious, undeliverable vanity projects such as online planners and interactive maps? The best advice is to visit local tourist information offices!

Hazards

A walk on a pleasant sunny day on Kinder Scout is a delight and it is difficult to imagine that it could ever be a dangerous place. But visit it on a cloudy, windy and wet day and its potential dangers become more apparent. Navigation becomes a much more significant challenge. It is very easy indeed to misjudge the scale of features in the mist, so that a tiny insignificant gully can easily look like a major gorge in restricted visibility. It is all too easy to go in the wrong direction, even onto dangerous ground. The weather can easily destroy paper maps, so on the more demanding walks be prepared for the unexpected and the potential for things to go wrong. Check the weather forecast before you start the walk (available from the Met Office website mountain area forecasts page).

For the landscape lover, the usual hazards of the hills are multiplied. Wandering off to look at rocks, views and so on can add significantly to the time needed for a walk and this should be taken into account, especially in the short days of winter. Thus the times suggested for the recommended walks in this book are somewhat longer than would be given in a general hillwalking guidebook (and include allowances for stopping to explore rocks and features, for contemplation and refreshment, for enjoyment and, hopefully, extra insight into the rocks and scenery).

Take very great care if you enter caves. Exploring old mines and quarries is particularly dangerous. Do not enter mines, tunnels or holes in the ground. In copper and lead mining areas especially, look out for open holes in the ground down which you could easily fall, never to come back up again! In quarries watch out for unstable rock faces which may, and do, collapse at any time. The same is true for waste tips which can be unstable, especially after heavy rain. Don't get too close to the edge at the top of quarry faces – those little gulleys running parallel to the cliff edge are tension cracks where the rocks are preparing to slip. From below, always look up as you approach a cliff or quarry face to see if there is anything that looks as if it is about to topple on you.

Be extremely careful in the areas of rock falls, especially below Mam Tor.

Finding more information

A geology map is extremely useful if you want to become more familiar with the different rock types. The British Geological Survey's most up to date 1:25,000 maps cover several areas of the Peak District and are the most useful (especially when used with the OS 1:25,000 map).

Sheet 08 – Matlock   Sheet 19 – Buxton   Sheet 24 – Monyash

Sheet 18 – the Roaches   Sheet 20 - Castleton   Sheet 30 – Bakewell

and Upper Dove Valley   Sheet 23 – Miller's Dale

There are also 1:50,000 scale geology maps which cover larger areas at the expense of detail.

Sheet 99 – Chapel en le Frith   Sheet 111 – Buxton   Sheet 124 – Ashbourne

A visit to the 'GeoHut' information and display centre about the geology of the Peak District at West View Farm, Alstonefield (www.geohut.co.uk) is highly recommended if you are anywhere close to the area. The GeoHut is located not far from walks 7 and 8 (Wolfscote Dale and Dovedale) just north of Alstonfield on the road towards Hulme End (postcode DE6 2FS). There's also a good display of various Peak District rocks, including a very good display of mined minerals, at the tourist information office/visitor centre at Castleton.

In the introduction I said that no specialist geological equipment is necessary, though a hand lens (x10) is handy for looking at very small detail. I can also highly recommend strong reading glasses for map reading and looking at medium detail in rock faces, such as fossils.

As matters on the ground can change (stiles for example can be moved or new fences can appear) some of the information about the walks may become out of date. I will try to post updates/details if or when I become aware of them on the website www.rock-trails.co.uk where readers can also contact me to inform me of errors and changes.

Entreaty

Please take note of the Countryside Code; the most important injunctions are to close gates and leave absolutely no litter. For geologists and landscape walkers there are a few more things to think about, listed in the Geologists' Code. The most important is to only remove already loose fossils or rock samples, and not to try and lever or smash them out of rock outcrops (near Winnats, you are not even permitted to take any loose samples). For everyone, the main goal is to use common sense in minimising the impact you have on the environment.

Walk #1 Kinder Scout

START	▶	EDALE STATION (1230 8535)
FINISH	●	CIRCULAR ROUTE
TIME	⏱	5 HOURS+
GRADE	⦿ NAVIGATION ● ● ●	(IN CLEAR WEATHER)
	⬣ TERRAIN ● ● ● ● ●	
	⬡ SEVERITY ● ● ● ● ●	

Kinder Scout is a real Millstone Grit mountain moor. Its flattish summit plateau covers a substantial area, virtually all of it smothered in heather and peat. The plateau offers tough walking with numerous boggy 'cloughs' that need to be crossed. Navigation is difficult enough in good weather and becomes all but impossible in bad conditions. However, along its sharp edges on the southern, western and northern limits of the plateau, the situation is quite different. There are still plenty of muddy tracks in wet

Kinder Scout

weather, but the paths are generally pretty clear (though still need to be treated with care in misty weather) and the views are much more varied than from within the great moor itself.

From the geological point of view, this walk reveals a variety of features visible in the rocks around and under foot. The route is along the southern edge of Kinder Scout, offering panoramic views over Edale to the Lose Hill, Mam Tor and Rushup Edge ridge as well as close encounters with amazing rock sculptures. The descent brings you down through Grindsbrook Clough, a real mountain valley (initially on a steep rocky track) with more fascinating geological features.

320 million years ago a distributary channel of a large river draining from mountains to the north carried down eroded material and dumped it into the sea, slowly building a delta. As the river channel met the sea, the heavier fragments of eroded material (sand) fell rapidly to the sea floor in the immediate area. However, lighter material (mud) was carried a bit further. Over time, as the end of the river was extended further out, the sand was dumped on top of the mud. Eventually the river stream overflowed its existing channel and a new channel developed. Over several million years, the whole area underwent prolonged but gradual subsidence. Layer after layer of mud and sand were laid down on top of one another which hardened to form shale and sandstone (sometimes known as 'grits').

Today, many millions of years later, one layer of sandstone is exposed on the edges of the summit plateau. The rough, gritty sandstone is known as the Kinderscout Grit (though it is also found elsewhere such as on the summit knoll of Win Hill, Offerton Moor and Eyam Moor). While there is plenty of sandstone to be seen, the softer shale is usually covered with vegetation and is rather shy. Nonetheless this route also takes you past an impressive outcrop of shale underlying the Kinderscout Grit. The exposed rocks are crumbling, cracking and slumping as they are undermined by a stream.

It is the relative strength of the two rock types which has produced the flat, sandstone-capped summit plateau with its sharp edges and makes it one of the most popular walking areas in the Peak District.

From east to west the plateau is about 6 kilometres long and from north to south is about 3 kilometres (though in its north-western corner it is less than 1 kilometre north to south and similarly it thins out to the east). The 'summit' itself is 636 metres high, though in fact the highest section runs south-west to north-east from Kinder Low at 633 metres in the south-western corner, via the highest point, to Crowden Head at 632 metres near the northern edge. This represents a slight bowing or folding of the rocks into a gentle anticline running north-south. On either side of this fold the plateau dips very gently away to the north-west and the east, only dropping to 590 metres around the Druid's Stone visited at the start of this walk.

From Edale station or the car park head north up the tarmac road towards Kinder Scout until a footpath sign is reached on the right at 124 586. Follow the footpath towards Ollerbrook Booth joining an east-west track among the complex of buildings at 1275 8590. Follow the track east towards Nether Booth. Just after crossing a fence at 134 856 bear left and follow the footpath towards the Youth Hostel at Rowland Cote. There are several access points onto the moor behind the complex of Youth Hostel buildings, but the best route is to go through the grounds round into the clough to find the stile leading to a path rising on the western side of Lady Booth Brook.

Follow this path up to the first side valley, noting occasional outcrops of sandstone, then break off left following the side stream up to about 1375 8685. From here it is worth taking a little time to view the surrounding scenery and to decide between a harder or an easier way to the edge. The first attraction of the scenery will undoubtedly be south towards Lose Hill and Back Tor where the landslip area (walk 2) is easily seen, but take time to study the slopes around you. The edge is visible on the skyline but below it the scenery is subdued, vegetation covering everything. Yet there is a pattern to the landscape here with flattish areas separated by short and somewhat steeper slopes. This is best seen looking across the clough to Upper Moor and the slope/shelf below it. These slopes and shelves are etched into the layers of sandstone and shale. The shale is easily eroded away, but the sandstone is harder and forms the top of each little rise. This is clear at the skyline, where the sandstone is exposed, but less obvious lower down where sandstone and shale alike are clothed in peat and vegetation.

From here decide on a route. The direct line involves heading a little west of north straight for the edge on the horizon. The going is rough and involves a small scramble to get onto the edge, but it takes you up close to the fascinating shapes of the weathered faces of some of the rocks of the edge which are not easily seen from above once on the edge (photo w1.1). The strange shapes of the weathered rocks are a key feature of this walk.

Kinder Scout

Photo w1.1 |

Weathering pattern on
slab of Kinderscout Grit.
Height of boulder 1.8m.

If you find the terrain too rough or bracken makes this direct route too difficult, an easier route can be found near the stone wall/fence marked on the map from 1375 8685 which meets the edge at 132 872 (though this takes you some way to the west of the Druid's Stone).

The Druid's Stone (photo w1.2) is slightly laid back from the edge and is best approached from the west, so some tramping over rough ground may be necessary. Certainly from the west one can appreciate the name, but not from the north-east where it appears more like two creatures engaged in some activity or other. It looks different again from other angles. Close up, it can be seen to consist of very gritty sandstone with small quartz pebbles clearly visible. The Druid's Stone is the first of many weird formations which will be seen on this walk, making them a key aesthetic as well as geological point of interest throughout. Naturally the shapes, with innumerable atmospheric variations, have attracted many painters and photographers as well as walkers and geomorphologists.

Return to the track along the edge and turn right onto it, following the edge as it swings between south-west and north-west for the next 3 kilometres or so towards the head of Grindsbrook Clough. The first feature on the way is Ringing Roger, a headland sticking out between Ollerbrook Clough and Grindsbrook Clough. The far end of the headland is a superb viewpoint along the edge to the east and the west, as well as across Edale to Mam Tor and Rushup Edge and the landslips on their northern flanks.

Ringing Roger's array of exposed tors forms a mass of wind-carved rock which mock the minimalist form of the Druid's Stone. These tors betray more clearly their geological structure in their shape (photo w1.3). The secret lies underfoot and in the wind that is almost always a feature of the weather here. The track is almost entirely made up of sand which has been eroded from the rocks. This happens because some of the sandstone is cemented with calcareous cement which was deposited in small amounts as lime mud. This breaks down chemically with the acid water of the peat bogs, releasing the grains of sand. If you pick up some of the lumps of sandstone on the track you will find that you can easily crumble them in your hand (but elsewhere, where the rocks are cemented with silica, they are very resistant).

Photo w1.3 |
Dramatic natural
sculpture, Ringing Roger.

Kinder Scout

The loose sand provides material for the wind to whip up and blast at the exposed tors. The tors here show that they are made up of harder and softer layers, with the later being more easily eroded. So we end up with the shapes that characterise this cluster of natural sculptures.

As you walk along the edges you may also notice that the sandstones are often different colours, some almost white, others brown or grey. These colours are determined by the way in which the rocks weather owing to their chemistry. When a rock is freshly broken it is immediately subject to chemical weathering from contact with the atmosphere and the acidic peat. However, the rock tors show that most rocks will eventually become grey, often covered in micro-lichen and visible lichen.

Continue along the track with superb views over Grindsbrook Clough to the hills beyond it which show once again the pattern of shelves and slopes, easily seen in profile on and below Grindslow Knoll on the other side of the clough (photo 3.2 and diagram 3.1).

At the head of Grindsbrook, at 1065 8745, the stream has eroded down into the rocks and exposed their slabby structure (photo w1.4). You can also detect the 'dip' or tilt of the beds, originally laid down horizontally but gently bowed by the distant collision of tectonic plates many millions of years ago. Kinder Scout is part of an anticline or upward fold that runs all the way up the Pennine range.

Photo w1.4

Tilted bedding exposed in dried-up stream bed.

Photo w1.5 | Rock sculpture, Woolpacks.

From here a number of extensions are possible. For more amazing stone sculptures a trip to the Woolpacks is essential (photo w1.5). For a much longer extension, the best route is to head via Grindslow Knoll and the Woolpacks to Kinder Low (photo 3.1). Kinder Low is only 3 metres lower than the actual summit, but the views are much better with the north-western edge and the eastern flanking hills easily visible. Kinder Scout's rock strata are only gently tilted in any direction.

Return to the top of the western feeder stream into Grindsbrook Clough (at 1055 8722) and descend into the valley. The way is steep and rocky for the first 100 metres or so, but the angle soon relents. Take your time and stop every now and then to enjoy the rock scenery.

After a few minutes keep an eye out for the appearance of an outcrop of shale on the left of the stream. There are sections of the shale which have broken and slumped as the stream cuts into the base of the outcrop (photo w1.6). This contrasts with the solid rocky edges seen earlier in the descent. The boulders at the top of the clough are all sandstone which has collapsed after being undermined by the eroding of the lower shales. The process is clearly seen along this extended outcrop of collapsing shale.

Photo w1.6

Slumped and crumbled

shale outcrop stream,

Grindsbrook Clough.

After a few metres the shale outcrop is replaced by another group of sandstone strata. The rock strata are usually hidden under vegetation but can be seen peeking through in places in the slopes under Ringing Roger above you on the left as you descend into the village.

Walk #2 Bretton Clough

START	▶	HOPE RAILWAY STATION (1805 8325)
FINISH	●	CIRCULAR ROUTE
TIME	◐	6 HOURS+
GRADE	◉	NAVIGATION ● ● ● ●
	☁	TERRAIN ● ● ●
	◈	SEVERITY ● ● ●

The traditional image of Millstone Grit scenery is of open moors covered by peat bogs and heather resulting in tough walking conditions and, except on the edges, views limited to wide open skies and vast tracts of rolling plateau. In fact the landscapes of the Millstone Grit are quite varied, partly as a result of human influence. This walk is entirely within an area underlain by the shale and sandstone of the Millstone Grit, yet it encompasses farmland, grassy moors, heather-clad moorland and wooded valleys.

This is an ideal way of getting to know the Millstone Grit without the rigours of Kinder Scout. There is even a small rocky edge with some interesting erosion patterns.

The most fascinating part of this walk is the 2 kilometre stretch along the valley of Bretton Clough where there has been a mighty landslide or landslides, leaving a strange hummocky landscape. The walk through the slumped area gives a real feeling for the power and size of the landslide. Some of the hummocks display their still coherent, horizontal beds of sandstone and shale, suggesting that they must have slid away from the main face intact. Landslides are a fairly common feature of the Millstone Grit as the tough sandstone is more resistant to weathering than the softer shale. Also sandstone is porous so that water can drain through the rock, but shale is impermeable and water has to find an escape route at the boundary between underlying shale and overlying sandstone. Landslides are likely to occur after heavy rain when the weight of the overlying rocks moves, lubricated by the water, and slides downhill.

Although the walk only ascends to modest heights, reaching a maximum of just over 400 metres, it is still a fairly long walk and requires concentration on the navigation via an intricate network of footpaths and access land.

From the station bear left along the lane towards Hardhurst farm (camping); at the T-junction turn right down to the main road. Cross the main road and head south on the B6049 using the pavement on the western side of the road. As you cross the bridge over the River Noe, an old mill can be seen to the right with remains of the waterwheel just visible. The mill race is now dried up. Continue south to the small junction on the left (1835 8261). Turn into the small tarmac track and follow it in an easterly direction to another junction (1845 8243); turn right and start to head gently uphill on a wide farm track. Highly fossiliferous lumps of limestone can be seen underfoot on the track as you ascend.

As height is gained the views start to open out over Shatton Moor to the left and to Lose Hill and Mam Tor to the far right. Despite the scenery, however, it is the Hope cement works which dominate the centre of the view of Edale, as it does from most directions. This close, it is also possible to see the extensive old quarry remains surrounding Eccles House Farm, located between you and the cement works. You can also see the massive gash of the present-day quarrying digging into the limestone uplands to the west of the cement works.

As the easy-angled climb continues the views become confined to the east, increasingly revealing Overdale Clough between you and Shatton Moor. Shatton Moor is made up of strata of sandstone and shale. The lower sandstones are given the contradictory-sounding name of the 'Shale Grits', though the summit layer is made up of the Kinderscout Grits. Shale separates the two sandstones. The rocks are not visible, coated by soil and vegetation, but express themselves in the layering with flat sections and steeper slopes. As you ascend, the layering can be seen curving round the southern flank of Shatton Moor (photo w2.1).

Photo w2.1 | Shelf and step topography on Shatton Moor from interlayering of shale and sandstone.

Carry on upwards, enjoying the increasingly fine views to the east, until a bridleway sign-post is met at 1825 8085. This is not quite where you might expect it to be from the OS map which shows the bridleway joining the track about 200 metres earlier. Turn right and follow the bridleway sign towards another stone wall which brings you out on Bradwell Edge. On the other side of the stone wall, bear right and follow the wall out to Rebellion Knoll (1812 8115).

The walk out to Rebellion Knoll provides more views of the cement works and its scenic setting, but the best views come when you turn round and return to the track. The walk back to the first stone wall offers fantastic views along Bradwell Edge and also across to the limestone plateau. If you look down in the valley, you can see the limestone cliffs of Bradwell Dale.

On returning to the track, continue south then south-south-east until you meet a set of stone stiles and notices at 1840 8026. Cross the stile and continue just west of south, with a stone wall on the left, up Bleak Knoll, to a very large wooden ladder stile at 1827 7965 (note that this section of the walk crosses from the OS 1:25,000 Dark Peak map to the White Peak map). Access land ends here and there is no right of way to the summit point (416 metres) just

300 metres to the south-east. Having enjoyed the views from here, cross the ladder stile and head on a bearing of about 150 degrees to meet the minor road from Abney where a marked footpath also meets it at 1890 7865. This section takes you across a gently bowed, grassy moor a classic Millstone Grit landscape.

As you approach the road it is worth noting the knoll to the east, Abney Low. This rich-looking grassland, with its pattern of radiating stone walls, is remarkable for the way it looks so different from the open moorland underfoot and to the north-east. The geology map, perhaps surprisingly, tells us that the rocks forming the Abney Low knoll are in fact rough gritty sandstones of the Millstone Grit. The summit rocks are actually the same rocks as those found on the summit plateau of Kinder Scout (walk 1) and are known as the Kinderscout Grits. Layers of shale separate the grits from lower layers of another formation of sandstones, the inaptly-named 'Shale Grits'. This is a classic example of 'improved' land on the Millstone Grit, mainly given over to pasture rather than to crops, and sporting sturdy-looking stone farmhouses.

The other feature to keep an eye out for as you cross the moorland is the valley into which you will soon be heading, Bretton Clough. The valley is carved, quite sharply, into the higher land to the south. Very sharp vegetated edges mark the top of the valley side. Two areas of slumping should be visible, marked by the presence of quite a few trees and curved sections at the edge of the deep valley sides.

On meeting the road, cross and go down a track (not marked on the OS map) to join the track heading towards Grange Farm and Abney Grange. A 'grange' was an outpost of a medieval monastery where the clerics' sheep would have been tended. Take the footpath to the right just before reaching attractive farm buildings and follow the track down into the valley, noting as you descend the views of the hummocky landslide area ahead. At the bottom cross the footbridge. From here you can see several rows of hummocks, almost like solidified waves. Head a short distance uphill, then bear left to a gate.

Take a moment here to look again at the knoll of Abney Low; its shape reflects on a minor scale the layering which is typical of Millstone Grit landscapes with shelves and steps.

Pass through the gate and follow the minor track as it passes along and between the landslide hummocks. From here it can be seen that there is an appreciable distance between the lip of deep section of the valley and the hummocks (photo w2.2). As you continue along the track you will notice that the hummocks are not, as might be expected, a mass of jumbled and broken rocks. Occasional outcrops of both sandstones and shales show that the strata have survived and have remained more or less horizontal (photo w2.3).

Photo w2.2 | Landslide area, Bretton Clough.

Photo w2.3 | Upper part of one of the blocks that has slid down the hillside while retaining the coherence of its strata.

Photo w2.4 | Slumped block.

Follow the minor track, keeping an eye out for a hummock way up on the right-hand side which, unlike other hummocks, has remained very close to the valley side (photo w2.4). This hummock is marked on the OS map as a ring contour at 1955 7830. It is very distinctive, being small and steep-sided and with a small capstone made of sandstone.

Go up to this hummock and pass between it and the valley side to get the best view of the capstone from the eastern side. It is quite obvious from the capstone and underlying layers that this hummock has retained its form even after it has become detached. It seems clear that the hummocks have slipped away on soft water-logged layers of shale from the main valley side and slid, in a coherent fashion without breaking up in places, to form the hummocks.

Drop down back to the narrow track, taking time as you do so to look back up the valley to see the array of hummocks through which you have passed. Looking back down the valley, Stanage Edge becomes visible in the distance. The main valley side starts to close in here, but will soon open out again to reveal another area of landslides.

Pass various rock outcrops and at 1995 7860 go through a gate and carry on to where there are the remains of an old building on the left. Walk left out past the remains to the lip of flat land for very clear views up and down the valley. The upstream hummocks are smaller and steeper-sided than those down the valley which are shallower and wider. There seem to have been two major episodes of landslide, the downstream landslide being the earlier one.

Carry on along the narrow track until you need to drop down, cross a tributary stream and pass through a gate. After going through the gate, follow the track up to the right for just a few metres into an open area. Leave the track which continues along the valley (unless you want to cut out the next section, in which case carry on to Stoke Ford where the recommended route returns to the valley).

Head due east up the slope towards a gap in a line of trees and towards a tumbled-down stone wall beyond. On reaching the stone wall, bear left and follow the wall along until it turns left across your path. From here aim for another stone wall off to the right and a ruined building at 209 788. Look ahead as you approach to see a small rocky edge directly ahead on the upper side of a valley coming in from the right (and to which the recommended route will take you). Go past the ruin and follow the track as it bends right into a small clough.

If the weather has not been too wet, drop down left from the track to the tiny noisy stream, hidden under vegetation, and follow it up to the entrance to a small gorge. In dry weather head up the gorge, taking care, or return to the track. Follow the gorge up to a fence and bear right up to a gate. If following the track, leave it where it swings sharply to the right and head for the gate directly ahead.

Go through the gate and up for a few metres until you can get down to the stream, noticing the pile of boulders in the middle of the valley. Cross the stream and head up to a stile in the fence above. After crossing the stile, head up diagonally left to meet the top of the headland at about 2122 7885, just short of the rocky edge. There are some interesting erosion patterns in some of the outcrops. The patterns are similar to those seen on the

direct approach to Kinder Scout as described in Walk 1. There are excellent views up Bretton Clough from above the edge and the size of the nearest landslide area is clearly seen extending well into the valley side (a diversion to some of the archaeological sites on Eyam Moor is possible from here). The layered topography on Abney Low is well displayed from this angle (photo w2.5).

Follow the track to the right well above the river course as it gently descends back into the valley, eventually swinging first sharp left and then sharp right, until you arrive at Stoke Ford. Follow the footpath signposted for Hazelford. Initially the track rises (again presenting opportunities to visit archaeological sites on Eyam Moor) then falls back down to the stream again. Cross the footbridge and rise up through Highlow Wood and then through a field aiming for the left of Highlow Hall and a minor road. Turn right along the road for about 50 metres, then turn left onto a track which should be followed towards Offerton Hall. From near Offerton Hall follow the bridleway until you meet the tarmac track going up to the mast on Shatton Edge. Initially there are excellent views of Millstone Edge and Stanage Edge, but increasingly the attention will be focused on Win Hill, the Derwent valley and Banford Moor. All are part of the Millstone Grit.

On meeting the tarmac track, turn right and follow the tarmac road down to Wheat Hay Farm then turn left along Townfield Lane, taking the footpath accessed by stone steps on the left a few metres along the lane. Follow the footpath until it ends, and follow the track

Bretton Clough

until met by two gates ahead. Take the right gate and follow the track until just beyond the first fence on the left, then turn right and walk up a low grassy bank to the top. A stile then becomes visible. Cross the stile and turn left, then follow the fence diagonally down to a field. Cross the field aiming to the right of the house. As you approach the house you can see what is known as a 'ha-ha', a ditch that acts as an invisible boundary (for those looking out of the house) which effectively keeps livestock out of the garden. You then are channelled to the right of a row of leylandii into a narrow, damp, insect-ridden track. The leylandii, one might well say, create an 'anti-ha-ha', being the antithesis in relief, far from invisible and not in the least funny. With that wry thought, follow the path to the road bridge at Brough and then to the railway station.

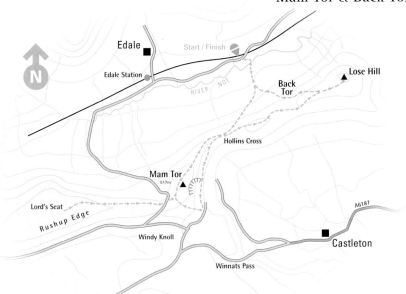

Walk #3 Mam Tor & Back Tor

START	▶	BRIDLEWAY (NO SIGN) (1365 8555)
FINISH	●	CIRCULAR ROUTE
TIME	⏱	6 HOURS+
GRADE	🧭	NAVIGATION ● ●
	☁	TERRAIN ● ● ● ●
	✖	SEVERITY ● ● ●

This route, which follows the finest ridge walk in the Peak District, takes you up close to some of the great landslides found in the Millstone Grit of the Dark Peak. Some 600 plus landslides/landslips have been identified by geomorphologists. This route allows you to study close up two of the more substantial of those landslides as well as affording an overview of others.

The Mam Tor landslide, overlooking Winnats and Edale, is justifiably famous. It has left an impressive rocky face on the southern side of Mam Tor. 'The Shivering Mountain' may only reach 517 metres, but it certainly looks like a real mountain thanks to the great rock face created by the landslide. However, there are three other landslides on the northern side of the ridge which tend to be overlooked by walkers speeding along the ridge top.

The ridge is the product of these landslides which cut back into the ridge sides, narrowing them. The oversteepened sides, which lead to landslides, are a product of the Ice Age and many slides were initiated during that period of intense cold. However, the landslides seen on this walk, though primed by glacial erosion, date from around 3,000 to 8,000 years ago i.e. after the glaciers had retreated.

The ridge is made up of layers of different sandstone, the Mam Tor Beds and the Shale Grit. Both these formations have some beds of shale interlaid between beds of sandstone and everything sits on a thick bed of shales, the Edale Shales. These shales are pretty weak and have undergone considerable crumpling and distortion when tectonic forces compressed the underlying tectonic plate towards the end of the Carboniferous period and after. The stronger sandstones and nearby limestones put up more resistance to the compressing forces at the expense of the Edale Shales, which show considerable intense folding and breaking up of the beds.

The sandstones sit on top of this weak, unstable foundation, creating the conditions for the landslides seen on this walk.

The fact that the Mam Tor landslide is still active is clearly seen in looking at the closed section of road, especially viewed from the north. Looking back from the path described in the route that rises gently from the landslide area to Hollins Cross on the ridge, the slow slide of the lower hummocks is palpable.

The recommended route is designed to give the walker a close-up look at some of the rock faces, rock falls and landslide areas and leaves the ridge line in two places (Mam Tor and Back Tor) to walk under the collapsed rocks. This is very atmospheric and instructive, but it is not without risks. It is not just the hummocks at the base of Mam Tor that remain active. The rock face regularly relinquishes its grip on small bits of rock and sizeable boulders, some of which can fall on the unwary. Beware of dangers and of the importance of not getting too close to the rock face. The Back Tor face is less active but still demands that you hold a reasonable distance.

The walk is described as beginning at Back Tor Bridge, about 1.5 kilometres east of Edale, but could easily be started from where the A625 road has been closed because of the Mam Tor landslide, where there are parking places and a bus service (see note at end).

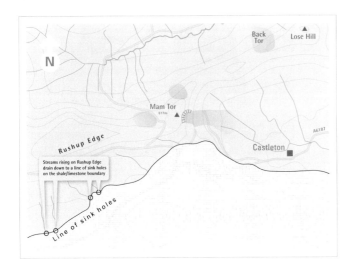

Back Tor

Lose Hill

N

Mam Tor
617m

A6187

Castleton

Rushup Edge

Streams rising on Rushup Edge
drain down to a line of sink holes
on the shale/limestone boundary

Line of sink holes

Map w3.1

Geology around
Mam Tor.

shale & sandstone

limestone

area affected
by landslips

Leave the road at 1365 8555 (bridleway, no sign) following the track down to the stream and across the bridge. Follow the track and signs past Back Tor farm up to a stone wall and gate at 1390 8513. Go through the gate and keep left alongside the stone wall. When the stone wall bears sharp left, turn half left (just south of east) and pass up through hummocks created by the landslide way above you. Pass through a gate in a stone wall at 1423 8500. The footpath continues right up to the ridge below Back Tor which is now visible in all its stony might. However, the recommended route breaks off left from the path and aims towards the base of the rock face.

There are traces of path, but you need to navigate a route between hummocks and boggy patches, typical features of the area of the slumped landslide mass. Well before getting too close to the rock face, keep left and work your way around to the north-eastern corner of the rock face, taking opportunities as you go to observe the rock strata with alternating layers of sandstone and shale (photo w3.1). The lower strata are part 'Shale Grits',

Mam Tor & Back Tor

a series of sandstones interleaved with shales, and the upper strata are part of the Mam Tor Beds with more strata of sandstone and shale. There is also a significant patch of shale separating these two formations at this point. So, unlike the large Mam Tor landslide where the underlying Edale Shales gave way (see below), it seems that the Back Tor slide occurred at a boundary between sandstones and shales. The landslide area is almost an amphitheatre, with a rounded backwall.

Photo w3.1
Interleaved resistant
sandstone and soft
shale on Back Tor.

Apart from the rock face, the two most impressive parts of the landslide are the jumbled mass of boulders and the extent of the hummocky landslide area which stretches all the way down to the river below. While you can see a lot of sandstone boulders about, there is very little evidence of shale. It is easily broken up and washed downhill.

From the north-eastern corner of the rock face, a small track rises to meet the ridge at its lowest point between Back Tor and Lose Hill. As you get close to the stone wall on the ridge line you will come across a very old boundary ditch, probably of medieval origin, parallel to a tumbled-down stone wall and a modern barbed wire fence. The track is between the stone wall and the fence and takes you in a couple of minutes to the top of Lose Hill. Here you will find wonderful panoramic views from Kinder Scout to the north, the twin knolls of Crook Hill and the isolated knoll of Win Hill as well as distant edges making nickpoints on the skyline to the east, and the vale of Eyam and the limestone massif to the south. The 'layering' of the fairly horizontal beds of sandstone and shale on these hills with respective steps and shelves is quite easy to discern.

When you start to walk west along the ridge, another fine new vista of the sinuously twisting ridgeline opens up in front of you. The views of Cave Dale and of Winnats, as well as of the big landslide on Mam Tor's eastern face, are particular points of scenic interest.

It takes only a few minutes to reach the top of Back Tor where the landslide area can be seen from above, but don't get too close to the edge of the rock face as the rocks forming the crest line are being undermined from below, as will soon become evident. The full extent of the flow of landslide material is best seen from this viewpoint, stretching all the way down the valley side to the river. Although the lower hummocks are less immediately obvious, they can still be seen within the enclosed fields.

Descend the short but steep ridge slowly, taking time every few steps to stop and appreciate the layering of sandstone and shale as you go. There is a particularly good example of the way shale is easily eroded, removing support from the overlying sandstone (photo 3.4). The sandstone block juts out quite a distance above the crumbling shale. This shale will soon be eroded further and this particular sandstone block will tumble downwards, probably along with a bigger collapse in the immediate area, and the sandstone block will join the others littering the foot of the rock face.

Continue along the track to Hollins Cross, a major crossing point of the ridge. The rise to the summit of Mam Tor is at an easy angle on a slab path. The points of interest here are views towards the Mam Tor landslide ahead, the gouges made by Winnats and Cave Dale into the limestone massif to the left and the edges and cloughs of Kinder Scout to the right. As you approach the summit area keep an eye out for the remains of the hill-fort bank (though this is most apparent later on the descent to Mam Nick).

Enjoy the views from the summit, especially back along the ridge to Back Tor and Lose Hill (photo w3.2), then walk over to the top of the rock face but do not get too close. This is an active landslide area and you can see the curved ('arcuate') gashes in the grass and soil near the edge. These are tension gashes, created as the rock face prepares to collapse at some point in the near future.

Photo w3.2

View from the summit of Mam Tor along the ridge to Back Tor and Lose Hill, with the eastern flanks of Kinder Scout on the skyline.

Mam Tor & Back Tor

If you wish to cut the walk short you can miss out the next section and follow the recommended route after it returns to Mam Tor (see below). Otherwise, descend on the slabby track towards Mam Nick and Rushup Edge. There are very good views of another landslide, on the right of Rushup Edge (photos 6.6 and w3.3).

Photo w3.3

Landslide on the northern flanks of Rushup Edge, seen from below the summit of Mam Tor.

As you approach Mam Nick you will be able to see an outcrop of the Mam Tor Beds shales and sandstones directly across the road (photo w3.4). Keep with the path until you are able to cross the road. It is then possible to backtrack somewhat to approach these exposures, but do so carefully as they are active and may slide. You can get a good feel for the weakness of the shales, contrasting with the strong sandstones. Ignore the main track (a popular cycling route) and ascend on the apex of the ridge and on to the summit where there is a tumulus. The views are outstanding, especially back along the ridge to Mam Tor and Lose Hill and also down to the landslide on the right.

Photo w3.4

Black crumbling shale with sandstone bed, Mam Nick.

There is little point in going any further as the ridge widens out from here and the views are less compelling. Return to Mam Nick along the ridge, taking the opportunity to study the pattern of the hummocky landslide area now on the left. There are also excellent views of Winnats as you descend.

From Mam Nick, re-ascend to the summit of Mam Tor. From the summit trig point head on a bearing of 150 degrees (or directly towards Winnats). This will bring you to the southwestern lip of the landslide area. From here there is a steep (slippy and muddy in the wet) descent. The steepness is worth putting up with as you get superlative views of the Mam Tor rock face from this descent. The layered nature of the Mam Tor Beds is clear to see (photo w3.5).

Photo w3.5

The main rock face of Mam Tor following the major landslide; note interlayering of sandstone and shale.

Pick a route carefully as you get lower down to meet the road at the point where it is closed 1314 8333. Those who wish to avoid the re-ascent of Mam Tor and steep descent can drop down from Mam Nick to the road junction at 1285 8310 and then follow the old road to rejoin the recommended route at the road closure point, but you will miss the excellent views of the rock strata.

Follow the road closure downhill for about 100 metres, noting the way in which it is clearly sliding down the hill. This is a useful indicator of the fact that the whole set of hummocks seen in front of you is slowly crawling downhill, creeping a little bit further into the valley floor every year. Below the rock face the whole hill is on the move. As the rock face is undermined, so new rocks will be shedded from above to resupply material for new hummocks. See chapter 6 for a more detailed account of the Mam Tor landslide.

Mam Tor & Back Tor

Once you recognise one landslide on the ground you will be able to recognise others, especially after studying those seen on this walk (or on the OS map where the contours take on very convoluted shapes, almost reminiscent of the loops seen in some fossilised algae). It still takes a leap of the imagination to appreciate that these particular hummocks are not stable features of an event that happened some time ago. The sliding roadway provides strong feeling that this is an on-going process rather than a one-off happening. Of course, erosion and levelling down of high land is going on over the earth's surface. It is a process that is hard to visualise, even when you see mountain streams in flood full of material being carried down. Here it is possible to understand that the landscape is not fixed, but constantly changing thanks to the peculiar mix of rock types present here.

There is a choice of two tracks from here back to Hollins Cross. A footpath which goes past Mam Farm leaves the slumped roadway where it does a sharp right-hand turn at 1325 8390. Alternatively, break left away from the road when you've seen enough of it and pick up a slightly higher but narrower track (which is slippery in wet weather). It will be easier to find the track if you look out for it on the descent from the summit and get an idea of where to head to meet it. On either track, remember to look back now and then for excellent views of the sliding road and the hummocky landscape. From Hollins Cross, follow the footpath towards Back Tor farm and back to the road.

To start the walk at the Mam Tor road closure, follow the closed road then one of the tracks to Hollins Cross and then follow the footpath towards Back Tor farm. You can either break off the footpath at about 1375 8475 and contour across to the gate in the stone wall at 1423 8500, or continue on the footpath until it meets the path ascending from the farm at 1390 8513. Once at the gate in the stone wall, follow the main recommended route instructions.

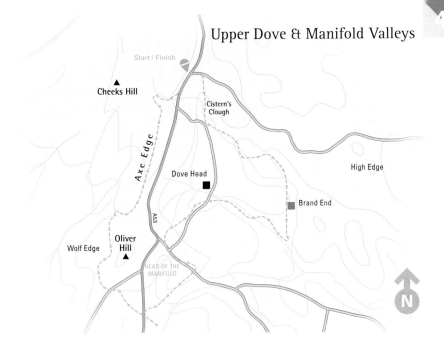

Walk #4

Upper Dove & Manifold Valleys

START	▶	DISUSED LOOP OF A53 ROAD (0350 6983)
FINISH	●	CIRCULAR ROUTE
TIME	◐	4 HOURS+
GRADE	◐	NAVIGATION ● ● ● ●
	◔	TERRAIN ● ● ●
	✖	SEVERITY ● ● ●

The valley of the Dove river is without doubt one of the Peak District's scenic gems, especially as Dovedale in its lower section between Milldale and Thorpe Cloud is one of its most popular visitor attractions. In fact, the whole of the Dove valley is of great scenic and geological interest. It is however quite a long walk if you want to see the whole valley, far too long for a single linear walk. This means that I had to decide whether to select part of the valley, making invidious choices, or cover the whole valley by splitting it into several walks.

Thus, five walks (this one plus walks 5, 6, 7 and 8) in this book effectively cover the whole of the valley (except for a few short sections). The walks cover its convoluted source among shale and sandstone to where it leaves the limestone gorge at Thorpe Cloud. All the walks follow a route near to the river for some sections, but all also trek upwards to high points for wide views all around from some of the best viewpoints of the White Peak, including Axe Edge (this walk), Chrome Hill (walk 5), High Wheeldon (walk 6), Ecton Hill (walk 7) and Thorpe Cloud (walk 8).

Arranging five circular walks also allows, on two of the walks, the chance to appreciate some of the valley of the Manifold River which rises right next to the Dove and eventually flows into it just south Thorpe Cloud.

This walk circumnavigates the heads of the Dove and the Manifold, observing some remarkable geological features as the head streams of both rivers cut through a band of tough sandstone in order to gain the middle reaches of their valleys. Walk 5 takes over where this walk turns back and ranges over some outstandingly mountainous little hills (Chrome Hill and Parkhouse Hill are both reef limestone) as well as pointing out other geological features. Walk 6 does a northwards loop from Hartington along the eastern side of the River Dove in its middle maturity, passing atop what I think is probably the best single viewpoint in the valley, High Wheeldon. Walk 7 includes a stroll through a section of the 'upper lower Dove' south of Hartington and then crosses over reef limestones and past old copper mines, ending up with a view of some incredibly intense folds in limestone rocks. Walk 8 brings us to the 'lower lower Dove' and its remarkable collection of rock 'tors', such as Lover's Leap and Tissington Spires, and offers the chance to see Dovedale at is prettiest from above as well as from below.

This intensive look at one river valley is fascinating for the geologist and landscape lover given the wide variety of valley shapes and situations. These are often determined by the geological structure but at other times seem to be insistently discordant with the geology. In its upper reaches, seen on this walk in some detail, the river transgresses the geological structure in a quiet but utterly determined fashion. The river rises in basins carved into the soft shales and then cuts steep-sided valleys through tough sandstone. The same is true of the River Manifold which rises just a few hundred metres from the Dove and must also find an escape route through the sandstone. This fascinating feature is seen in detail on this walk.

Having escaped through the sandstone, the River Dove in its middle reaches lies roughly on the boundary between the limestone to the east and various shales and sandstones of the Millstone Grit to its west, as seen in walks 5 and 6. In its lower section, seen in walks 7 and 8, the Dove has again managed to cut a deep, steep-sided valley and, at a couple of points, a narrow gorge right through the Carboniferous Limestone.

The recommended route on this walk starts with a short climb and walk along Axe Edge, providing an overview of the head of the Dove. It then heads over Oliver Hill before descending to see the way the Manifold has carved its course through the sandstone. The route then crosses into the shallow valley of Dove Head before tracing its course through a narrow valley. We finally return to the start point with a section through another two narrow valleys alongside a subsidiary stream.

Axe Edge and Oliver Hill are obvious watersheds, with streams draining either to the west or east. A study of the map or of the terrain (from the southern side of Oliver Hill) raises the question of why the Manifold in particular drains south-east and not south-west down a more obvious course south of the watershed (to join the Dane). The Manifold rises just north-east of the village of Flash and flows south-west towards the village. Instead of joining up with springs to the south of the village, just short of those springs it suddenly does a U-turn, cutting deeply through the sandstone to head off north-east, performing a tight U-bend to turn its back on the obvious route.

What makes the Manifold take such a non-obvious route, cutting deeply through sandstone? Similarly, why do the Dove head streams also cut through this tough rock and not seek easier escape routes? These are the questions we will tackle on this walk and will be worth pondering on when ambling through the remarkable steep-sided gorges on the recommended route. In walks 7 and 8 we will be asking the related question: why did these rivers carve a way through apparent barrier of the line of limestone hills seen south of Hartington? The River Dove is fascinating not just for its setting and surrounding scenery but also for the apparent oddness of its river course.

Upper Dove & Manifold Valleys

The start point (0350 6985) is at a disused loop (in the original turnpike route) in the A53 road about 3 or 4 kilometres south of Buxton. Cross the stile at the head of the loop and follow the track up on the right of the stream. When possible cross the stream and then head up to the left when the slope relaxes (at about 0320 6985). Bear left towards the edge of Axe Edge, then aim for a small triangular boulder at about 0328 6958 (photo w4.1). This is an example of one of the rough sandstones or 'grits' within the Millstone Grit group, known as the Roaches Grit. The underlying large grains of sand making up the rock are clearly visible even though covered with red, green, grey and white lichen.

Photo w4.1 + w4.2 | (Left) sandstone boulder on Axe Edge. (Right) Cistern's Clough (centre left behind the road), with low-lying area to left of Hollins Hill and Chrome Hill.

Carry on up towards the summit along the edge of the ridge. This route makes a good place from which to study the head of one of the Dove feeder streams (Cistern's Clough) and the section of Dove valley down to Chrome Hill. However, if the weather is unkind, it may make sense to study the landscape below you from the road before setting off rather than from the edge of the Edge (photo w4.2).

From the top of Axe Edge, the steep hillside below you is the 'scarp' slope of the Roaches Grit. The 'dip' slope runs behind you much more gently. This pattern of slope is the result of tectonic movements (created by the collision of continental plates) which pushed the rocks of the area in a large 'anticline' or dome-shaped fold (with a corresponding but smaller downfold or syncline to the west on the line from the Goyt valley to the Goldsitch near the

Roaches). Axe Edge is on the western flank of the major anticline and erosion has exposed its tough face in the steep slope. Below the edge, in the bowl below the road, the bedrocks are softer shales and more easily eroded, thus forming the low land (map w4.1)

Map w4.1 | Geology of the heads of the Dove and Manifold Valleys.

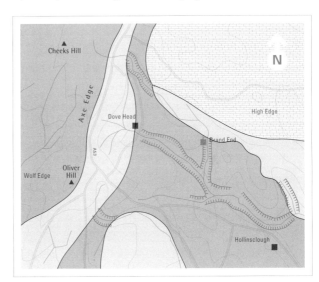

Beyond the basin below the A53 road there is some higher ground. This is another formation of sandstone, known as the Longnor Sandstones. The stream in Cistern's Clough can be seen dipping down towards the higher ground, exiting the basin in the softer shales through a narrow, steep-sided valley in sandstone (the recommended route returns via this valley).

Further down the valley the stream suddenly turns sharp right and passes through another narrow valley (not visible from here, but seen later in the walk) to join the main Dove river (which rises in another shale basin below Oliver Hill). What can be seen from here in the middle distance is the boggy, shallow basin just beyond where the stream does its sharp right turn near Chrome Hill and Hollins Hill (photo w4.2).

Having appreciated the view and thought about its components, follow the tiny track along the top of the Edge towards Axe Edge End. Follow the track to Hilltop and then to Oxenstitch where a footpath heads south for Oliver Hill. As you ascend Oliver Hill you can see that the footpath follows a narrow finger of 'improved' land poking into moorland on either side. Further up, looking left, you can see a sharp difference between the grazed and ungrazed areas.

Upper Dove & Manifold Valleys

When you meet a ruin at 0247 6772, stop and turn round to view the landscape behind you. Axe Edge's sharp scarp slope is immediately obvious, as is its shallower dip slope. Behind the track (with three separate farm houses strung out along it) another scarp slope, Drystone Edge, can be seen; a third edge can be viewed beyond that. The landscape then flattens out. The edges represent the turned-up scarp slopes on the eastern side of the Goyt-Goldsitch syncline, while the flatter ground to the left is the flat bottom of the syncline. Beyond it rise the dip slopes of the turned-up west-facing scarps of the same sandstones and grits as seen on Axe Edge and Drystone Edge.

As you turn southwards to continue the walk the bulk of the Roaches dominates the landscape, though there are also some small but rocky and distinctly prominent edges seen almost directly ahead as you descend. These also represent the west- and east-facing scarps on either side of the same syncline. There are also good views down into the head of the Dane valley on the right.

Head down into Flash then take the footpath next to the church through a farm lane and past a recycled petroleum tanker. Bear right and follow the footpath across the field to meet the main road at 0295 6682. As you cross the field you can see some edges in the medium distance. Less immediately noticeable is the valley that forms in the field below the footpath, heading down to Flash Bottom and then the Dane valley.

Cross the main road to the two footpath signs. The route will follow the left-hand sign, but first take a short diversion of about 100 metres out along the right-hand footpath to get a view of what is happening here. From a suitable viewpoint on this footpath, near where it bends right, turn round and look at the course of the River Manifold. The river rises in a basin behind the hillside through which the river flows. It can be seen coming down a narrow, steep-sided valley and then turning sharp left to pass through another narrow valley below you. At the end of this narrow valley, it turns left once again and picks a course in a much wider valley with steeper ground to the left and shallower ground to the right (photo w4.3 and diagram w4.1).

From the geology map it can be seen that the basin in which the river rises is an area of shale squeezed between two thick layers of sandstone. One layer of sandstone forms Axe Edge and Oliver Hill to the left. The other layer forms the headland opposite you which runs up to Summerhill and the headland on which you are standing. Somehow, the river has cut this steep-sided valley through this sandstone. A casual glance at both the topographical and geology maps suggests that a more likely course for the river would have been to cut a channel in line with the geological strata; that is, heading south-west down into Flash Bottom

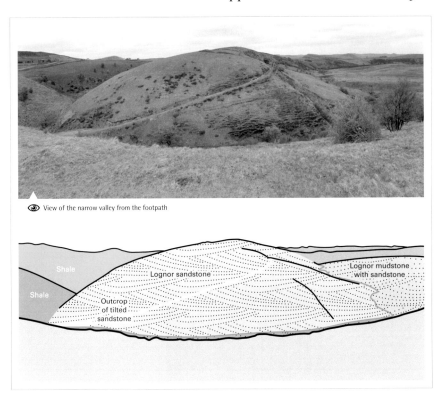

👁 View of the narrow valley from the footpath

Shale

Lognor sandstone

Lognor mudstone with sandstone

Shale

Outcrop of tilted sandstone

Diagram w4.1 + Photo w4.3 | Panoramic shot of stream cutting through layers of sandstone.

through the valley seen in the field just before the road. Instead the river, more a tiny stream at this stage, has cut this convoluted and rather improbable course through the sandstone.

The answer must be that the river course is a very old one with a long-established route which has imposed itself on the existing surface geology.

This feature is known as 'superimposed' drainage. The ancient river course was initially determined by the geology of the overlying rocks (rocks that have now been fully eroded away). The river has managed to preserve its old course despite meeting new geological conditions.

Another theory suggests that superimposed drainage may develop during the slow process of tectonic uplift (due to the collision of continental plates). The rate at which the land was pushed up and folded into anticlines and synclines was so slow that the river was able to maintain its previous course by eroding the rising land as fast as it was pushed upwards.

However, this would mean that the river course was very ancient indeed and had survived millions and millions of years in its present course, implying that the erosion theory is the most likely in this case.

Whatever its origin, you are observing a fascinating feature. Think back to the valley in the field crossed before reaching the road. This is in the soft shales on the same side of the sandstone as the head of the Manifold, yet the river has ignored this possible escape route preferring instead the sudden turn through the tougher sandstone, cutting through it rather than the easier shales.

To continue, return to the road and follow the other footpath (a tarmac track) down into the valley. As you descend you can see ahead an exposure of sandstone with dipping beds (photo w4.4). Follow the track up Nield Bank, taking the muddy track up left after the farmhouse, to a stone wall. Take a look around here for the fine views, especially towards Hollins Hill, Chrome Hill and beyond.

Photo w4.4

Tilted sandstone bedding, with beds ranging from 50cm to less than 1cm in thickness.

Take a few minutes to absorb the whole panorama. Starting on the far left the skyline is High Edge. This is classic limestone scenery with plenty of rock outcrops (distinguishing it from the rounded, wholly vegetated slopes of the Millstone Grit areas, both shale and sandstone, apart from the occasional outcrop on the edges). Then moving to the right comes Hollins Hill (with a small landslip on the lower slope below its highest point) which is made up of sandstone.

Beyond Hollins Hill, there is again limestone scenery. Chrome Hill, Parkhouse Hill, Hitter Hill, the prominent High Wheeldon and beyond to Pilsbury, are all limestone 'apron reefs'. The Dove has now found a course to the immediate right of these limestone reefs with Millstone

Grit rocks to its right. These rise gently to form a scarp slope above the Manifold along Edgetop. To the right of the Manifold, further dip and scarp slopes can be seen.

Carry on along the footpath to join the road at 0369 6741; turn left and walk along the road. Once past Summerhill farm you can see the start of the Manifold valley in the field to the left. Carry on towards the A53 until you reach the footpath at 0326 6780 and follow it down into the basin in which the Dove rises. Descend initially alongside the Dove stream, then cross the stream and head down to meet the tarmac track at 0360 6810.

Again, take a moment to observe the landscape. The shallow basin sits at the bottom of the southern end of Axe Edge. It is made up of soft shale. The streams meet at 0385 6830 on the boundary of the shale and the sandstone and then enter a narrow, steep-sided valley to escape the basin through the sandstone. This is quite similar to what we saw with the River Manifold (though without the sharp U-bend).

Follow the tarmac track down to where the streams collect near the entrance to the narrow valley. Cross the stile on the right and follow the footpath, initially high on the right of the valley, then drop down into the valley and cross a footbridge at 0430 6812. Bear right and follow the footpath further down the valley initially high up, then descending again. This will bring you out to the junction of two valleys at 0510 6760. Follow the footpath back up to the top of the valley side of the valley coming in from the left

This roller-coaster route will give you plenty of opportunity to appreciate the exact steepness of the valley sides and to note how far the stream has cut down into the sandstone on its escape route. Follow the path to Brand End: from here the stream buts up against limestone on the eastern side.

At Brand End descend once again towards Thirkelow. From near Thirkelow look back to the south-east (towards Booth Farm) to a low, wet basin. Here we have a similar situation to Flash where the Manifold abjured a course on the shale to cut through the sandstone. Here the tributary of the Dove has turned sharp right and cut through 50 metres of sandstone, while straight ahead the land rises only 35 metres (photo w5.6).

At Thirkelow turn left towards Brand Side, but at 0457 6880 bear sharp right and then left and head for Fairthorn (0427 6917). It is immediately noticeable that the area around Brand Side is much less confining than the valleys followed for the last 2 kilometres or so. Brand Side area is another basin in the softer shale. If you drop down to the footbridge at 0430 6910 you can see outcrops of crumbling shale on either side of the stream (photo w4.5).

From the footbridge, return to the footpath that passes through Fairthorn and follow it as it starts to ascend gently with Cistern's Clough stream on the left. Here you enter another

Upper Dove & Manifold Valleys

sandstone area, marked by a narrowing and steepening of the sides of the valley. Some sandstone outcrops can be seen in the river side and also some minor waterfalls. In some the 'dip' of the rocks can be seen. On reaching the bridge at 0387 6952 you can turn left up the track and then follow a minor road back to the start point, or you can carry on up alongside the stream having crossed so that it is on your right. After about 150 metres at 0382 6968 there is a small outcrop of crumbling shale. This is marked on geology maps as a 'fossil locality'. This may sound exciting, but published fossil localities generally tend to rapidly become ex-fossil localities. Carry on to the minor road at 0380 7015, turn left towards the main road and then left back to the starting point.

This short walk back along the road allows time to get a last overview of the basin in front of you. Consider how the landscape around here is a product of interleaving of hard and soft rock, gross tectonic forces and the insistent power over time of a river to incise its chosen course whatever the obstacles put in its way.

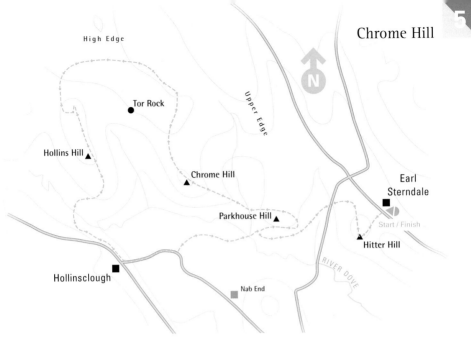

High Edge

Tor Rock

Upper Edge

Hollins Hill

Chrome Hill

Earl
Sterndale

Parkhouse Hill

Start / Finish

Hitter Hill

Hollinsclough

RIVER DOVE

Nab End

Walk #5 Chrome Hill

START	▶	VILLAGE GREEN AT EARL STERNDALE (0900 6700)
FINISH	●	CIRCULAR ROUTE
TIME	◷	4 HOURS+
GRADE	◉	NAVIGATION ● ● ●
	◔	TERRAIN ● ● ● ● ●
	✪	SEVERITY ● ● ● ● ●

This is the second walk in the series of five walks covering virtually the whole of the valley of the River Dove (see walk 4 for a general introduction to all five walks). This route starts with Hitter Hill (just a short walk from the village of Earl Sterndale), crosses the very narrow and steep ridge of the tiny Parkhouse Hill, and then crosses the somewhat less narrow and less steep ridge of the bigger Chrome Hill. After that it strikes out along the edge of a very different shape of small hill, Hollins Hill. These

Chrome Hill

pocket-sized hills certainly provide some frills as well as views and are also geologically fascinating.

The River Dove runs below these hills, crossing tough sandstone to find a course on shale close to the boundary line between the Millstone Grit and the Carboniferous Limestone. Hollins Hill is part of the Millstone Grit, formed of sandstone and standing proud of the surrounding shale. Hitter Hill, Parkhouse Hill and Chrome Hill are all examples of limestone reefs, though the last two are surrounded by softer shale. This contrast of rock types, along with fault lines that run across the area, has resulted in the stunning shapes of the isolated knolls of Parkhouse Hill and Chrome Hill.

These are two quite small hills. Parkhouse Hill can be crossed in less than thirty minutes (if you don't linger to enjoy the views and study the rock outcrops). Nonetheless these miniature hills are truly at the centre of visual interest from whichever angle and distance that they are seen, far or near. Fittingly, they are also fascinating in detail as well as in general. They are often described as like waves, frozen in motion as if by a photograph. Indeed, the asymmetric profile of both hills, steeper on their northern flanks and slightly convex in shape on the southern side, does almost give this impression.

In fact both hills have faults on their northern flanks which have thrust the ridges above the level of softer (and later) shale in the area between them and to their north and east where the limestone plateau becomes continuous. This has allowed erosion to work on softer shale, resulting in a sharp almost vertical slope down to the north on both hills. This fault is best seen on Parkhouse Hill's northern slope (photo w5.1).

As a result Parkhouse Hill is pretty steep and narrow and great care should be taken on ascent, crossing and descent. It may not suit everyone as a head for heights is essential. The crossing is best avoided in high winds as you might easily be blown off the sharp ridge line.

Hollins Hill has a very different shape from the two limestone reef hills and provides superb views as well as interesting contrasts between the limestone areas and the sandstone/shale areas.

Start from the village green at Earl Sterndale by heading for the footpath to the right of the pub, the Silent Woman (the 'joke' being that she has no head). Follow the left-hand path to the summit of Hitter Hill for superb overviews of the Dove valley and the walk ahead. On the other side of the valley the shapely Nab End is conspicuous. It owes its shape to the fact that it is made up of two sandstone layers at the top, forming the sharp edge and its sharp end, and shale on the lower slopes (indeed the shales come all the way across the valley, past the river and road at Glutton bridge right up to the boundary of the access land below).

The shale also crosses into the area between Hitter Hill and Parkhouse Hill (and also further on between Parkhouse Hill and Chrome Hill). Thus there are broad basins that almost cut off Parkhouse and Chrome Hills from the main body of the limestone. On leaving Hitter Hill you will cross one of these shale basins. Note the line of old mineral workings which can be seen crossing the summit area of Hitter Hill, following a seam containing lead (photo w5.1).

Photo w5.1
View from Hitter Hill to Parkhouse Hill and Chrome Hill; remains of mineral workings on Hitter Hill in foreground.

Chrome Hill

From the summit head down to the stile on the B5053 at 0845 6682 either steeply and directly or less steeply by first heading towards the footpath coming from Earl Sterndale, joining it at 0860 6695 and then to the stile. Follow the footpath across the road and through fields to the edge of access land at 0810 6677, then turn right. The limestone used in the stone wall contains lots of fossils. Follow the wall up to the base of Parkhouse Hill and look up the steep slope to the top. This is thought to have been part of the seabed, dipping steeply down from the shelf or platform. However, where you are standing is not the bottom of the reef's outer sea-facing slope. Later shales have been formed so the outer surface of the reef goes much deeper, out of sight under the ground. Geologists reckon the steep reef slope must go on for many more metres before the sea bed of that time is reached.

If you decide to miss out the climb and descent of Parkhouse Hill, from here bear left and follow the base of the hill round to its eastern end to rejoin the recommended route. Keep an eye out for fossils to be seen in rock exposures.

For the recommended route, turn right and follow the wall below the eastern end of the southern edge of the hill. Some of the Millstone Grit sandstones can be seen in outcrops as you walk along here. At the end of the ridge, bear sharp left and strike steeply upwards picking the least onerous-looking route.

Going over the hill provides a thrilling combination of height, steepness, stupendous views and fascinating outcrops of reef limestone. What is most striking are the rocky knolls that are passed on the way. The limestone towers become ever more impressive on the descent at the eastern end. Later in the walk, returning below the hill on its southern side, these knolls can be seen to form a series of vertical forms in the limestone. This is caused by 'jointing' in the limestone (drying out joints created soon after the sediments were laid down) that have since been eroded away by acidic rainwater dissolving the limestone.

From the eastern ridge and summit of Parkhouse Hill there are excellent overviews of the shale area between Hitter Hill and Parkhouse Hill leading up to Glutton Grange. More reef limestone is seen starting just behind the Grange, leading into the two dry valleys of Glutton Dale and Hatch-a-way. This geological pattern is due to the fault line that marks the northern sides of both Parkhouse Hill and Chrome Hill. The same fault runs on behind Stoop Farm (between Chrome Hill and Hollins Hill).

Other faults in the area to the north of both hills mark the northern limits of the shale areas. The shale areas have dropped down between these faults relative to the limestone reef areas, leaving these isolated shale basins between the rows of hills. One of the faults actually passes between Parkhouse Hill and Chrome Hill running north-west to south-east; the result is this complex pattern of reef limestone and shale basins. In one place (see below) the shale is topped by sandstone (the same layer of sandstone indeed that forms Nab End on the other side of the Dove valley).

Another feature to note is Nab End to the south, on the other side of the river. This self-confident pose is carved into sandstone, thus forming the prominent cap feature on the northern tip. The sandstone, which is tough but porous, lies on top of shale which is weak but impermeable. This means that rainwater can soak through the sandstone, emerging back onto the surface when it meets the shale. The spring line runs south along the valley, each farm marking a spring. On the northern tip a gully can be seen starting halfway down the slope, again marking the spring line. There is also a spring line on the eastern side of the valley where the limestone meets the shale, and again it is marked by the presence of farms (photo w5.2).

Photo w5.2

Nab End, upper part, porous sandstone, lower part, impermeable shale; spring line level with the farms, left.

Photo w5.3

View from Parkhouse Hill towards Chrome Hill along the line of a major fault marking the near-vertical slopes of both hills. Shale in basin (centre), shelf limestone (rising ground extreme right).

The steep, stony descent (needing very great care when the rocks are wet) leads you to the path towards Chrome Hill (aiming to meet the minor road at 0767 6710). The views are distracting and require you to stop frequently and soak them up (photo w5.3). The walk up Chrome Hill is easier because it is less steep and it is possible to keep away from the steep northern edge. It is a longer ascent, though still a modest one.

The views back towards Parkhouse Hill and beyond are worth stopping for every so often. The steep northern slope of Parkhouse Hill (on the line of a fault) is most impressive from here. Similarly, the shale area between Parkhouse Hill and Chrome Hill is clearly seen extending to Dowel Hall where the reef limestone begins again. This is clearly evident from the dry valley of Dowel Dale.

The higher ground to the north and north-east is mainly limestone. This is fairly clearly seen in the rock outcrops. The exception to this is the area north-east of Tor Rock. This area is sandstone, present here due to faulting. The area around Tor Rock itself and the upper part of Swallow Brook, below Hollins Hill, is again limestone (and it is the main 'shelf limestone', not reef limestone). The sandstone north-east of Tor Rock is an 'outlier', separated from the rest of the sandstone to the west (whereas the shale areas poking into the hills are actually contiguous with the main shale areas to the west). This underlines how complex the geology is in the whole area around here due to faulting.

The summit of Chrome Hill is another superb all-round viewpoint with magnificent vistas of the upper and middle sections of the Dove valley and of the hills all around. More interesting rock outcrops are seen on the descent from the summit. The well-worn track leads you to a 'concession' path that bears right (at 0670 6772) and heads uphill for a short time.

Photo w5.4 |
Natural arch on
Chrome Hill.

Photo w5.5 |

Millstone Grit sandstone,
left on Hollins Hill and
lower left section of valley;
Carboniferous Limestone,
right ridge line and upper part
of valley where the river twists
in the centre of the photo.

Photo w5.5 |

Millstone Grit sandstone, left on Hollins Hill and lower left section of valley; Carboniferous Limestone, right ridge line and upper part of valley where the river twists in the centre of the photo.

Photo w5.6 |

Low area between Carboniferous Limestone to right, Millstone Grit sandstones and shales to left.

Follow the path to the farm track (at 0645 6820) and follow the line of the footpath that circles round towards Booth Farm. As you near Booth Farm, keep well to its left on the tarmac track. Break off the footpath at about 0580 6795, and head left up Hollins Hill following the footpath signs (though it is actually access land). You will pass some sandstone outcrops on your right at around 0587 6784. These coarse sandstones (also visible in an edge to the right) are heavily covered in multicoloured lichen of reddish-brown, grey-white and green-yellow.

Follow the signs to the summit of Hollins Hill where there are excellent views towards Axe Edge and the head of the Dove. This is a good point to look at the 'superimposed' drainage pattern at the head of the Dove (see walk 4), but the best view is from the northern edge of the summit. The Dove rises in shale areas just east of Axe Edge but, instead of flowing south-west via more shale areas, the river has cut narrow, steep-sided valleys through tough sandstone to drain to the south-east past Chrome Hill into the middle Dove valley (photo w5.6).

The route of the stream from Cistern's Clough is fairly obvious from near the summit of Hollins Hill. The area where the stream rises is visible, as is the narrow, steep-sided valley through the sandstone that carries the stream into the wider shale area around Brand Side.

The stream then heads towards the low ground running between Stoop Farm and Booth Farm but, invisible from here, the stream does a 90-degree right-hand turn at Brand End Farm to cut another narrow, steep-sided channel through the sandstone (to join the Dove at 051 676 – see walk 4 which follows this narrow valley). It looks as if the stream should continue towards the farms and beyond to drain into the main valley between Chrome Hill and Parkhouse Hill. The story told by this drainage system on top of the present-day surface is complex and this is a great vantage point for studying the routes chosen by the Cistern's Clough river.

From the summit follow the boundary wall of access land along the north-eastern edge of Hollins Hill overlooking Swallow Brook. It may seem as if the valley bottom marks the boundary between the limestone on the Chrome Hill side of the valley and the sandstone and shale of Hollins Hill. In fact, a big chunk of limestone sticks out this side of the river in the upper part of the valley. A small part of it forms the outcrop of Swallow Tor and, in the lower half of the valley, the shales run right up to the base of the steep south-western facing slope of Chrome Hill along the line of the intake wall. There are great views of the middle Dove valley and especially Nab End from this unexpected little ridge walk (photo w5.7).

All too soon the ridge ends and a convoluted track takes you back on to a right of way at 0615 6705. Turn left and follow the footpath down to and across the Dove on a charming little bridge. The path then leads to the road just above the hamlet of Hollins Clough. Turn left on the road, take the next left and after about 400 metres, turn left onto a farm track (a 'byway open to all traffic') which leads across farmland below Chrome Hill to a road. The marvellous views are only spoilt by the proliferation of 'private land' notices around this area, perhaps made necessary by the few rights of way in the area leading to lots of people taking short cuts.

Cross the road and pick up the footpath which crosses below Parkhouse Hill, rejoining the outward route at 0810 6677. Follow the outward route to the start of the access land on Hitter Hill (at 0855 6690) and then the footpath roughly north and then east back to the start.

Photo w5.7 |

View of Dove valley,

Hitter Hill extreme left,

High Wheeldon, upper

left skyline; Sheen

Hill, distant right.

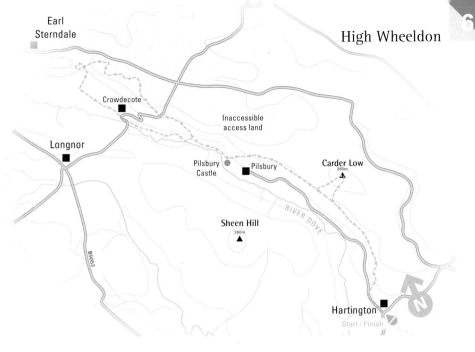

Walk #6 High Wheeldon

START	▶	HARTINGTON VILLAGE (1280 6042)
FINISH	●	CIRCULAR ROUTE
TIME	◔	5 HOURS+
GRADE	⌒	NAVIGATION ● ● ●
	☁	TERRAIN ● ● ●
	✪	SEVERITY ● ● ●

This is the third walk in the series of five walks covering virtually the whole of the valley of the River Dove (see walk 4 for a general introduction to all five walks). This route starts at the village of Hartington and follows footpaths along the middle reaches of the Dove valley before climbing to the majestic viewpoint of High Wheeldon. The return leg is high up on the valley side, using access land (where accessible).

The scenery on this walk is perhaps less spectacular than in the area around

High Wheeldon

Chrome Hill and Parkhouse Hill (walk 5) and in the lower sections of the Dove where the river cuts a narrow channel through the limestone (walks 7 and 8). Even so, from the hilltops (especially High Wheeldon) the views are extremely far-ranging and the valley is utterly charming.

From the geological point of view, the walk runs roughly along the boundary between the Carboniferous Limestone and the Millstone Grit and allows a study of the contrasting shapes of the valley sides. The limestone slopes are steep and steady with lots of small rock outcrops, although there are irregularities such as the limestone reef outcrop on which Pilsbury Castle was built. Between High Wheeldon and Pilsbury the limestone slopes are made up of 'reef limestone', while between Pilsbury and Hartington the valley sides are formed from a platform of 'shelf limestone'. The recommended route also includes a visit to view a small section of 'limestone pavement' on Carder Low on the return section. Limestone pavement is a feature common in other limestone areas of Britain, but is sadly largely absent from the White Peak and this is about the best example you will find in these parts.

The Millstone Grit slopes are smoother and lack the rock outcrops. They are not a smooth steady slope but form clear 'steps', the result of the interlayering of tougher sandstone and softer shale. There are several small landslips to be seen on these slopes and these too are the result of the interplay of the sandstone and shale.

The valley is fairly wide and shallow, especially compared with the upper and lower sections of the Dove (walks 4, 7 and 8) where the river has cut deeply down into tough rocks (sandstone and limestone in the upper and lower reaches, respectively). Nonetheless this section adds to the immense variety of landforms created by the Dove River as it has cut down into the bedrock, superimposing its course on exposed ancient sea beds.

A note of warning: watch out for an unfriendly dog just beyond Crowdecote. Cattle graze the fields on the route and some can be a bit aggressive, though most are not even curious. Be especially careful if you have a dog with you; the advice now is to let the dog go if cattle should approach you. That is not much help of course if you don't have a dog to let go of, so be prepared to retreat and think about possible escape options.

The walk starts from the village centre of Hartington, heading north on a minor road past the substantial village pond. Follow the road for about 400 metres to where it does a sharp right turn followed by a sharp left turn. Just at the start of the left turn, there is an unsigned vehicle track on the right (shown on the OS map as a 'white lane' and marked with three green spots). The vehicle track soon turns into a truly delightful green country lane (especially in spring when I was last here), with great views of the forthcoming walk over the stone wall on the left of the lane.

On reaching a minor road, turn left and follow the road up towards a farm building complex where the road swings right. Just after the farm, cross the stone wall to follow the signed footpath across fields towards Madge Dale. The footpath brings you out above Bank Top Farm.

There are good views here towards High Wheeldon on the recommended route and also across the valley to Sheen Hill. The distinction between the valley sides is immediately obvious with distinct layers marking different levels on the Sheen Hill side and a more constant slope on the High Wheeldon side. The eastern side of the valley is underlain by limestone and the western side by a mix of sandstone and shale. The intermixing of the layers of softer shale and more resistant sandstone (all of the Millstone Grit) results in the steps, with level(ish) areas separated by sharper slopes. The elegant profile of Sheen Hill illustrates the scenic results of this differential resistance to erosion.

Look for the two landslides on the other side of the valley roughly opposite Bank Top Farm. They are distinguished by hummocky ground and something of a cut into the skyline at the top of the slope (photo w6.1). These landslips are caused by softer shale being eroded away with overlying more resistant sandstones being undermined and eventually collapsing.

Photo w6.1 | Landslide area on opposite side of Dove valley, near Bank Top Farm.

High Wheeldon

Follow the footpath across more fields for about 900 metres until you come across a series of pits and tips running in a line diagonally across the footpath. These are the remains of old mine shafts working a seam of metal-bearing minerals. Another line of pit remains is passed after another 600 metres or so. There is also a third line of remains somewhat higher up the valley side near the top of Carder Low.

Geology maps of the Peak District show a series of mineral seams running across much of the main limestone areas of the White Peak. Nowhere do these seams cross into the Millstone Grit, which was laid after the limestone. The conclusion is that the seams were intruded (by superhot liquids and volatile elements shooting up cracks or faults in the earth's crust during times of tectonic activity) before the Millstone Grit rocks were laid down. There are several clusters of such seams in the White Peak, often running either north-west to south-east or roughly south-west to north-east. Many are quite short, only a few hundred metres long, but some can run for several kilometres. The metallic minerals are usually found within a seam of calcite.

The three lead-bearing seams around here are just a few hundred metres long; all run north-west to south-east and all three are on the line of faults. The little pits and surrounding tips also have a plugged shaft entrance, so it is clear that the seam was worked by digging shafts every so often rather than by cutting a rake. This suggests that the seam must run reasonably deep.

The stone wall crossed shortly after meeting the first line of pit remains is the boundary of the access land area around Carder Low. It is well worth making a short diversion up and back down Carder Low to see the fragmentary limestone pavement near the summit. I have included this as part of the return journey and deal with it below, though there is no reason why you shouldn't climb up now rather than later if you prefer.

To carry on, ignore the vehicle tracks passed after the second line of pit remains and stay on the route of the footpath up to a stone wall crossing at 1250 6330. Cross the wall and head down to the floor of the dry valley, then turn left and follow the footpath towards a farm building. Just before the farm building cross the road and follow footpath signs pointing you well to the left of the building.

Shortly the headland on which Pilsbury Castle was built comes into view ahead along with superb views up Dove valley towards the distinctive 'wave-like' shapes of Parkhouse Hill and Chrome Hill (photo w6.2). Pilsbury Castle is actually part-built and part-natural. The natural part is on the right, a clear outcrop of reef limestone imitating the shape of the up-valley hills. The built 'motte' is seen to the left of the natural outcrop; the 'bailey' occupied

Photo w6.2

Pilsbury Castle, left, is built on a natural outcrop of reef limestone; Chrome Hill visible in centre distance.

Photo w6.2

Pilsbury Castle, left, is built on a natural outcrop of reef limestone; Chrome Hill visible in centre distance.

the area between the motte and the outcrop. The castle was probably built around 1100 AD by the new Norman lordship. Much of the area was taken over later by the international network of Cistercian monasteries which introduced intensive sheep-grazing and more thorough exploitation of farming lands.

The footpath takes you right up to the castle grounds and over to the rock outcrop. The outcrop is actually an isolated exposure of the reef limestone surrounded by shale (of the Millstone Grit), though it is only a very short distance until you find more reef limestone. The limestone can be seen just behind the stone wall at the base of the slope in the scattered outcrops on the hillside (the limestones are linked out of sight below the overlying shale).

Further up the valley, Parkhouse Hill and Chrome Hill are both made of reef limestone and are similarly cut off from the main body of the limestone (walk 5). Their isolation is due to the presence of faults that have led to the lowering of the area separating them from the limestone platform to their east. The lowering of the land has brought softer shales to the present-day surface and these have been eroded to leave the two shapely hills standing proud.

There are no faults shown on the geology maps of the Pilsbury area, so some other explanation is called for here. After the end of the deposition of the limestone and before the start of the deposition, of shales (of the Millstone Grit Group of rocks), the area was probably above sea level for some time and subject to erosion. For some reason, this isolated knoll of reef limestone was eroded around leaving a rock tor; this is not unusual in limestone and such isolated tors can be seen in the limestone gorge of the lower Dove (walks 7 and 8). More examples can be seen in other limestone areas such as along the coastal cliffs of the Gower peninsular in South Wales which are also Carboniferous Limestone. As the raised land around might well have been at the edge of a sea, this is possibly what happened here.

High Wheeldon

The area was then inundated again, slowly subsiding under sea level. Millions of years of deposition of the Millstone Grit rocks got underway, beginning with the shale which was deposited on and around the whole area including on top of the main platform limestone. In the many more millions of years since then, the overlying rocks have been slowly eroded away until the core of the limestone was exposed at the surface. Erosion, however, has not yet reached the stage of carrying away all the shale that was deposited behind the isolated rock tor. Erosion will continue and, in a few more hundreds of thousands of years, more shale will be carried away until the underlying limestone connecting the main body and the isolated knoll is exposed at the surface and the apparent isolation ended.

Head down towards the outcrop, but bear left in front of and below it to a small and more easily accessible outcrop on the right. The reef limestone here is highly fossiliferous and lots of remains can be seen in the small lumps that have eroded off the bedrock. Take some time to enjoy the castle and then return to the path via the north side of the isolated outcrop observing the reef limestone rocks. Regain the footpath and head north-west along the flattish valley floor. The bank of the other side of the river rises quite sharply from the river here, maintaining the asymmetry which is such a feature of the valley sides on this walk.

The limestone boundary is roughly along the line of the stone wall marking the lower boundary of access land, so the actual river course is entirely on top of shale. The two sides of the valley are so clearly different: on the one hand, the limestone supports a thin soil with rocks visible all over and on the other, the Millstone Grit rocks support a thicker soil and a wider variety of vegetation. The stepped nature of the western valley side is also observed from around here, especially the view of a now elongated Sheen Hill.

The reef limestone protrudes outwards from the main western valley slope as you approach Crowdecote, and the footpath reaches the base of the steep slope just before Bridge End Farm. Go through the farm track past the farm buildings and carry on to the road at 1008 6510, turn right and almost immediately left at the next junction on to the minor road running below High Wheeldon. Turn right on to a public footpath through Meadow Farm. (Watch out for an aggressive dog that tries to get behind you and nip your ankles; a walking stick would be handy here to encourage it to keep a safe distance.)

The footpath joins Green Lane at 0955 6592. Turn right and after 200 metres join a minor road. Follow it up steeply through the short, narrow dry valley between High Wheeldon on the right and Aldery Cliff on the left. Glimpses of a quarry face can be seen on the left as you ascend. The quarry land has been acquired by the British Mountaineering Council and is now access land so it is possible (remembering that rocks do fall off the face so don't get underneath overhangs) to get a look at the limestone face of the quarry. This is part of the main platform or shelf limestone, not the reef limestone seen at Pilsbury.

To carry on, take the footpath from opposite the quarry entrance, initially north-east around the northern side of High Wheeldon. You'll pass a natural outcrop of the same limestone to your right. Follow the footpath to where another footpath joins from the left at 1020 6617. Here turn sharp right and follow the steep track up the hillside to the summit of High Wheeldon. Hopefully you will have good weather, allowing you to spend some time here soaking up the delicious views. This is an utterly fantastic 360-degree viewpoint with nearby hills and distant skyline competing for your attention (photo w6.3).

Photo w6.3 |

View north towards Nab End and Chrome Hill from High Wheeldon, one of the best all-round viewpoints in this part of the White Peak

This is probably the best viewpoint of the whole of the Dove. Axe Edge can be discerned on the skyline, under which the Dove rises. Below Axe Edge is the sandstone ridge where the Dove and its tributaries must cut a steep, narrow course before reaching the wider open area around Chrome Hill and Parkhouse Hill. The wide section of the middle of the Dove valley can be seen from those hills running below you and on towards the barrier of limestone beyond Hartington, through which the Dove must again cut a steep, narrow course.

There is a cave on the northern side of the hill, but it is hard to locate on the OS map. One of the highest caves in England, it appears that the cave was repeatedly used by early inhabitants (often to bury or commemorate their deceased) right up until the post-Roman era. Archaeologists have recovered Neolithic pottery and a Roman bronze armlet, among many objects. A skull of a bear was also found, placed in a way known to have been practised between 6,000 to 12,000 years ago in this region (when much of the area would have been wooded).

The walk heads back to Hartington using the newly designated access land that is shown running in a fairly continuous strip from here to near Pilsbury on the top of the limestone slope down to the valley floor. There is a small track to show the way which rounds a dry valley and then heads down to meet the road at 1035 6510 where there is a sharp bend. The next strip of access land is entered from the gate about 25 metres up the road on the right. Again a narrow track shows the way, guiding you down to Pilsbury Castle. I kept along the access land boundary up to 1170 6410 and found no way to continue on the supposed access land to the high point and cairn at 1206 6395. I later checked access from the other end from 1222 6358 to 1240 6365, but found no means of access. So, for the time being, it is necessary to return to the Castle and follow the outward footpath route from there back to 1257 6270 and the boundary of the access land around Carder Low. Cross the stone wall and bear up left towards the top of the hill.

The effort to reach the hilltop is worthwhile for the excellent views south to the next stage of the Dove valley. Better still, there is a small section of limestone pavement that you meet on the way up. This area is part of the main shelf limestone, there being no reef limestone between Pilsbury and Hartington. This small section of limestone paving is the best I have seen in the Peak District, but is quite small compared with outcrops in the Malham area of the Yorkshire Dales or the spectacular examples in the Burren in western Ireland (photos 7.1, 7.2 and w6.4 below).

There are two theories about limestone pavements. The first is that the soil was irreparably damaged by deforestation in pre-historic times and was blown away by wind as it broke down to leave bare rock. The second is that limestone does not naturally create a soil as the rock is dissolved by rainwater and carried away by streams and underground water channels; what soil there is on limestone must have been blown in by the wind from other areas. From the summit, having taken in the extensive views, head back down to the footpath and retrace your outward route back to Hartington.

Photo w6.4

Fragmentary limestone pavement on Carder Low

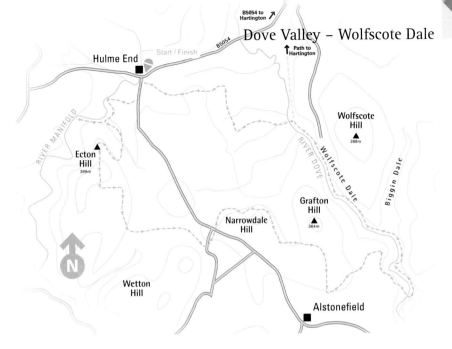

Dove Valley – Wolfscote Dale

Walk #7

Dove valley – Wolfscote Dale

START	▶	HULME END (105 925)
FINISH	●	CIRCULAR ROUTE
TIME	☕	6 HOURS+
GRADE	🧭	NAVIGATION ● ● ● ●
	☁	TERRAIN ● ● ●
	🗲	SEVERITY ● ● ●

This walk traces a route through a variety of limestone landscapes including part of the Dove valley known as Wolfscote Dale. It climbs to the top of a limestone 'apron reef', introduces a highly fossiliferous limestone, views the Dove and Manifold valleys and takes in a display of exuberant bending and folding of rock bedding in limestone.

Dove Valley – Wolfscote Dale

The walk also encompasses views from the confined, writhing limestone gorge of Wolfscote Dale to the panoramas atop Narrowdale Hill and Ecton Hill.

From Chrome Hill to south of Hartington, the Dove runs roughly along the boundary between the Carboniferous Limestone to the east and the Millstone Grit to the west. This middle section of the Dove valley (except around the Chrome Hill area) is magnificently pretty but not dramatic (walks 5 and 6). Yet about 1.5 kilometres south of Hartington the river suddenly carves a course into the upstanding limestone that has, from Chrome Hill, formed a guiding boundary on the river's eastern side. What causes the river to suddenly transgress against the underlying geology in this way?

This is an example of 'superimposed' drainage, probably due to the river having established its course on rocks that were laid down on top of the limestone, but which have now been entirely eroded away. The river continued to cut its established course when the limestone became exposed, resulting in a meandering gorge. The gorge provides a cross-section through the gentle tilting (or 'dipping') of the limestone beds. Most of the valley side slopes are covered in a mix of scree and grass, allowing us to see how scree and grass interact.

The walk leaves the gorge to head for higher ground of first Narrowdale Hill and then Ecton Hill. These hills offer fantastic oversights of the middle reaches of the Dove and Manifold valleys, presenting the landscape lover with some fascinating geology lessons. The limestones of these hills are highly fossiliferous in places. Ecton Hill is also famous for its old copper and lead mines and workings.

Finally, a short diversion heads into the start of the Manifold gorge (which is similar in origin and present-day character to Wolfscote Dale) to view some mightily impressive folds and faults within the limestones at Apes Tor.

The walk is described as starting and finishing at Hulme End, but could also be approached from Hartington. From the pub at Hulme End, head south on the road. This road is generally fairly quiet all the way to the Dove near Beresford Cottage at 1280 5860. Alternatively a route can be found using footpaths through the campsite 150 metres south of the pub and heading for Endon House, Lower Hurst farm and then Beresford Lane and Beresford Cottage. If you follow the footpaths, shortly after crossing the stream after the campsite you will pass an outcrop of crumbly shale in the stream bank illustrating how easily shale is eroded away.

Map w7.1 |

Geology of the
Dove Valley and
Wolfscote Dale.

shales of
the Millstone Grit

platform limestone

reef limestone

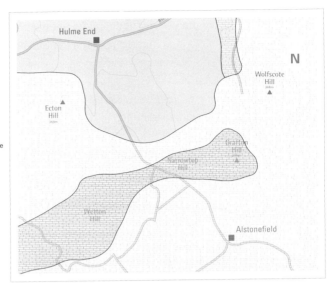

Photo w7.1 |

Bedded limestone upper
left; massive, unbedded
limestone, lower section;
cave lower right.

Cross the River Dale on the footbridge near Beresford Cottage (join the recommended route here if starting from Hartington) and then turn right, crossing a flood plain to enter the narrow gorge of Wolfscote Dale. Immediately you enter the gorge, a limestone outcrop is seen on the left with a cave in its lower part (photo w7.1). The cave and its entrance are highly polished by generations of inquisitive walkers and fossils can be seen around the entrance.

Continuing down the gorge, once you go round the first bend you can see the beds of limestone tilting gently from lower left to upper right on the left slope. Further on, the same tilt can also be seen in the limestone on the right slope.

Dove Valley – Wolfscote Dale

At first there are few rock outcrops and the valley sides are covered in scree and grass. The scree is still 'active' in places, as it is clearly creeping forwards over the path. On the slope next to the path you can see how the grass is slowly spreading itself over the scree where it is inactive, binding it in to form the valley side. You can also see how in places the scree collects on slight ledges formed by the tilted beds of the limestone bedrock.

Some way down the valley on the left of the track, you can see a section of scree that runs all the way up the valley side to a rock 'tor'. Here the slope is steep enough for the scree to keep the whole area free of grass. This is just before the first side valley comes in from the right on the opposite side of the main valley (photo w7.2). The outcrop on the right side of the valley is known as Drabber Tor.

Photo w7.2 'Hanging dry valley' joins Wolfscote Dale at a higher level than the main valley floor

Carry on down the valley until 150 metres after Biggin Dale joins from the left where there is a footbridge. The shortest option is to cross the bridge and climb steeply up to the tor above to a magnificent viewpoint. Alternatively carry on for another 750 metres or so to the next footbridge (Coldeaton Bridge) and cross here making your way up a slightly less steep slope. Take time for a small diversion left at the top for views further down the Dove gorge.

Turn round and head roughly north back up the valley, following a narrow track roughly parallel to the stone wall along the top of the valley side. An utterly delightful view of the gorge is gained from this section of the walk. After a few short minutes, at 1410 5665 you meet the footpath coming in from the first footbridge.

Follow the footpath/farm track to 1340 5605 and turn right. Follow the farm track to 1333 5650, appreciating the views to Gratton Hill, and then follow the footpath across a field as it turns from heading north-west to west to 1265 5668. Turn right and follow the footpath towards Narrowdale Hill to meet access land at 1265 5700. The footstone in the stile is a highly polished limestone with lots of crinoid fragments.

Head towards the rock outcrop which, as you approach it, opens out into a small bowl. The rocks are highly fossiliferous. Head to the top of the hill and find a good viewpoint to spend time soaking up and appreciating the geology and scenery arrayed before you to the north.

Starting on the right, the immediate neighbour is Gratton Hill. Like Narrowdale Hill, Gratton Hill is an 'knoll reef' limestone formed at the bounds of the limestone platform. Wolfscote Hill, beyond Gratton Hill, is part of the main limestone but is not a reef. The main platform limestone continues up on the right side of the Dove valley, forming a distinct undulating plateau that suddenly falls steeply away to the valley floor.

There are still remnants of reefs below Wolfscote Hill, but they peter out before Hartington. There is a small reef just south of Hartington and it can be seen forming a small tongue or knoll protruding from below the village towards the river. Again there is another stretch of the main platform limestone unaccompanied by reefs from Hartington to Pilsbury. From Pilsbury to Chrome Hill the reefs again become significant features in the landscape, especially the shapely Parkhouse and Chrome Hills.

The slope down from the limestone plateau to the river around the Hartington area is quite clear and is also very different from the slope of the valley on the west side of the river (diagram 5.3). This can be seen to rise in two steps or 'edges'. Sheen Hill is the top of the highest point; this hill and the lower edges are formed from tough sandstones interlaid between softer beds of shale.

Further left, the Manifold valley is rather different. It is a wide, shallow valley, situated in the middle of a syncline or downfold (caused by massive tectonic movements over very long periods of time causing the rocks to fold and deform). The rocks underlying the section of the Manifold in front of you have been folded only very gently over a wide area; later in the walk at Apes Tor much sharper folds on a smaller scale will be seen.

Though the two rivers (the Dove and the Manifold) flow in nearly parallel courses in their middle sections, they occupy very different geological foundations and seem to conform more to the demands of that geology than the upper and lower sections (walk 4 for the upper Dove and this walk for the lower). Here they flow either along a rock boundary at the base of a tough upwards slope of limestone or in the middle of a gentle downfold.

Take a little time to take in the distant views of Axe Edge, below which both the Dove and the Manifold rise. Much closer, look at the bottom of Narrowdale Hill at the dry limestone valley at the foot of the hill; notice how the vegetation changes colour and becomes much rougher than the other side of the dry valley. This change in vegetation marks the boundary between the Carboniferous Limestone and the Millstone Grit. Before moving on look south over the lower Dove and Manifold valleys and the limestone plateau through which they have cut their courses.

From the summit area of Narrowdale Hill aim for the corner of a stone wall at 1210 5730 overlooking the steep front of Narrowdale Hill's western flank. Follow the wall along (with the wall on your left). When the wall turns left carry on in the same direction as before alongside a stand of trees on your right. At the end of the stand of trees start making your way down to where the stone wall boundary to access land meets a tarmac track at 1170 5720 (this point is not directly visible from the end of the stand of trees). Pick a way down over a steepish slope but take very great care as there are old quarry workings between you and the tarmac track. They are best avoided by aiming well to the right of the grid reference above or traversing towards the stone wall and descending near to it, rather than taking a direct line.

Follow the tarmac track up to a minor road, cross and follow the minor road south-west for about 300 metres to where it bends sharp left. Cross the stile into the field and follow footpath heading just north of west to the foot of Wetton Hill, another part of the knoll reef. Follow the footpath which circumnavigates round the east and then the northern flanks of Wetton Hill. Leave the footpath at around 1095 5690 and head to a shallow area at 1055 5700 where springs make the area boggy at times. From here cross into the field and follow a footpath heading north-west diagonally across the field to a track at 1038 5715.

Turn right onto the track and follow it to 1043 5760. Turn sharp left and ascend a steepish slope towards quarry waste tips seen on the skyline. Take care with this section of the route where old mine ruins and shafts can present danger to the unwary. The rocks in the waste tips are highly fossiliferous with crinoids and other remains and fragments (photo w7.3). Some of the old mine shafts were sunk a couple of hundred metres down, lower than the level of the deeply incised Manifold valley on the other side of Ecton Hill. Both copper and lead were taken from around here. Most of the White Peak metal mines have yielded lead, but Ecton is unusual in having been a major source of copper.

From the top of the ridge, turn right and follow the footpath to the summit trig point. Go a bit further beyond the trig point to get a view down and along the Manifold Valley (photo w7.4). Follow a zig-zagging set of footpaths to the minor road at East Ecton (1030 5830) and then follow the road to a junction at 1070 5866. Turn left here and follow the road for 100 metres or so observing the display of sharply dipping, curving and displacing of folds in the rocks on the left. This is known as Apes Tor (photos w7.5 and 5.3).

Photo w7.3 | Copper mine waste tip on summit of Ecton Hill; Wetton Hill, centre right skyline, Narrowdale Hill, left distance.

Photo 7.4 | Remains of copper mine, summit Ecton Hill.

Photo w7.5 | One side of tilted beds of an anticline just topping out right of the photograph; variable thickness of bedding in dark ramp limestone, Apes Tor.

Photo w7.6 | What looks like a pile of loose scree is firmly cemented together by calcium carbonate re-precipitated on contact with the atmosphere.

The beds in the first outcrop can be seen clearly to bend over forming a small, rounded anticline. Just beyond this there appears to be a break in the beds. Then there are several sections with very sharp folds. The rapid alteration of the tilt or dip from up to down and back again is remarkably different from the gentle continuous dip seen in the limestones early on in the walk through Wolfscote Dale. The rapid alternation of small-scale syncline and anticline is also in distinct contrast to the wide, gentle syncline which affects the rocks on either side of the Manifold valley, as was seen from Narrowdale Hill.

Dove Valley – Wolfscote Dale

The limestone in Apes Tor is known as the Ecton Limestone and was deposited in a ramp off the side of the main limestone platform. It is a fairly impure limestone with quite a bit of mud or clay mixed in. This means that it is less resistant than the purer limestones of the main platform limestone and also less resistant than the Millstone Grit to the north. When tectonic forces from the collision of continental plates pushed the crust in this area into folds, the less-resistant Ecton Limestone was much more severely affected than the tougher rocks on either side, producing the intense folding seen here in Apes Tor.

Turn back and follow the minor road back to Hulme End. However, if you wish to extend the walk by 30 to 45 minutes, from Apes Tor continue down the Manifold valley. Carry on until you come to some parking places on the left of the road underneath great scars in the limestone slope leading up to the top of Ecton Hill around 0965 5820. The feature of interest here are some clumps of what looks like a rough gravel behind the fence at the bottom of the slope. Carry on walking until you come to a clump that extends to a point where you can try to pull lumps out. You will soon discover that what looks like a loose clump of gravel (just as you might see beside the road) is actually solidly cemented together (photo w7.6). This is small bits of scree that have fallen off the slope which have been cemented together by calcium carbonate re-precipitated from water emerging from the limestone. Many types of sediment take many thousands of years to cement into hard rock (which doesn't matter if the rock is going to be around for many millions of years), but limestone cement can act very fast as this 'gravel-stone' shows. Fast-acting cement is also thought to be behind the formation of reefs (or mud mounds) in the shallow tropical seas where the limestone was laid down.

Return to Dale Bridge and get on to the old railway line, now a cycle and footpath, and head south. As you follow the path you can see several exposures of the limestone, including one striking syncline (photo 2.6). Carry on to an obvious outcrop with a small notice post informing you that this is a Regionally Important Geological Site (RIGS) location. (There was a signpost at Apes Tor too, but it is so insignificant that it is easily missed.)

You can tell it's an important spot for geologists as the vegetation has been cut back and there is a considerable amount of fragmented rock (hammered away by specimen hunters). It makes sense that geologists must gather samples for close analysis but not everybody needs to have a sample in order to know exactly what this important outcrop contains. It seems a pity that the scheme that is listing sites that need protection are, instead, inviting damage to them. The answer to this problem must be self control, that is, less hammering rather than less publicity for the sites as these places are important for widening our knowledge and understanding. Turn around and return to Hulme End via the old railway line.

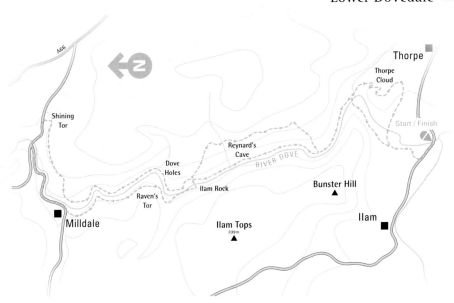

Walk #8 Lower Dovedale

START	▶	ST MARY'S BRIDGE (1470 5102)
FINISH	●	CIRCULAR ROUTE
TIME	◔	5 HOURS+
GRADE	⊙	NAVIGATION ● ●
	☁	TERRAIN ● ●
	⊗	SEVERITY ● ●

This is the fifth and final walk in the series of five walks covering virtually the whole of the valley of the River Dove (see walk 4 for a general introduction to all five walks). This walk starts and finishes near Ilam at the foot of two shapely limestone hills, Thorpe Cloud and Bunster Hill, and takes in views from below and above of the magnificent scenery of the deep incision made into the limestone by the River Dove.

Just south of Hartington (walk 7), the River Dove enters the limestone massif and emerges some 8 kilometres away at the start/finish point of this walk. The twists and turns the river takes during its course through the limestone almost doubles the distance actually travelled by the river (and the length of the walk alongside its course).

This whole section of the valley, from a short way south of Hartington to Thorpe Cloud and Bunster Hill, is an example of 'superimposed' drainage; the river's course was determined many years ago when the limestone was entirely covered by later rocks. Since then, the later, overlying rocks have been eroded away. The river has continued to cut its pre-chosen course down into the limestone to ensure that it can pass through the high mass of limestone that separates the lowland of the Dove's middle section (walk 6) from the lowland south of Thorpe Cloud and Bunster Hill.

The rock architecture left by the river as it cut its course into the limestone is remarkably beautiful, as suggested by the evocative names of some of the rock 'tors' such as Tissington Spires, Jacob's Ladder and Lover's Leap. The long kilometre of the valley between Tissington Spires and Pickering Tor is a true narrow gorge with the rock walls, deeply covered with vegetation, rising up from the river bed in the most dramatic section of the river Dove.

The unbridled beauty means that this whole lower section of the Dove is extremely busy and seldom a day passes without great crowds making their way along the valley. The recommended route, however, provides a way of maximising the enjoyment from the scenic charm of Dovedale and avoiding, for some of the time at least, the dense throngs on narrow valley floor tracks. This is achieved by using footpaths and/or access land that allows you to walk along the top of the valley slopes. These high-level routes offer some of the best views of Dovedale as it winds its way roughly north. They also allow you to see more easily some of the many side dry valleys that 'drain' into the main valley, gaining a good overview of the whole complex.

All the same, to get the best appreciation of Dovedale's scenic enchantment, it is necessary to follow some of the way at valley floor level. The recommended route picks some of the best of the lower tracks, including the section through the narrow gorge between Pickering Tor and Tissington Spires.

Another low-level section of the return route (between Milldale and Ilam rock) follows a narrow track on the right-hand side of the river looking downstream (whereas the main track is on the left side). This is a fine little track, much better than the main track. It takes you up to several limestone crags, including Raven's Tor where two types of limestone (reef and platform) can be seen.

However, this track does have one drawback: a short section of it disappears underwater after heavy rain at the foot of some vertical limestone cliffs. As the crux section is at the southern end of the track, near Ilam Rock, it is not really possible to be certain that the route will be fully passable until you get to near the end of the section of track; if you try to use this track in wet weather you may have to face returning to Milldale. Also, after heavy rain the track can be pretty muddy and may be hard work, so if in doubt it may be best to use the main track.

The walk climbs to the top of the hills or valley sides three times on the outward journey, but not at all on the return leg. If this is too much it is easy to leave out any of the climbs and stick to the valley floor. If, on the other hand, the day's recommended route offers insufficient hill-climbing, then it is possible to add an ascent of Bunster Hill at the end of the day. Unfortunately there is no easy route to the summit to link into the walk through and above Dovedale, so it is necessary to use the footpath from near the car park in Dovedale to gain access land on Bunster Hill's south ridge (or start from Ilam at the bottom of the south ridge). From the southern side Bunster Hill is, in my opinion, one of the most shapely hills in the Peak District and the walk up to and along the summit ridge is truly worth the effort. From the summit area, the overview of Thorpe Cloud is magnificent (photo w8.6).

From St Mary's Bridge (or the car park 400 metres up the lane) head into lower Dovedale. Cross the first footbridge at the foot of Thorpe Cloud and follow the boundary wall into access land round to the south-eastern corner of the hill and then turn sharp left and pick a way up the steep slope to the summit. (The steep climb and descent of Thorpe Cloud can be omitted by following the river bank path from the footbridge to the stepping stones, but use the footbridge in wet weather.)

The summit is a great view point. Noticeable at the bottom of the hill is a mass of medieval field strips still evident in the modern fields. Thorpe Cloud itself is thought to be a knoll reef or a limestone mud mound. It is not very clear to geologists why or how these mounds form, but it is generally assumed that they must have been rapidly covered by some form of sticky film secreted by micro-organisms. The film binds or covers the mound, helping

Lower Dovedale

to cement it and hence prevent it from being washed away by currents or tides.

There are knoll reef limestones on either side of Dovedale (photo w8.1) as far as Raven's Tor, and more such features above the valley beyond Raven's Tor. The reefs sit on and/or are interleaved with dark 'basin' or 'ramp' limestone which was deposited in a basin or low area at the edge of the main carbonate platform. Both the basin and the reef limestones are among the earlier Carboniferous Limestone strata. They are now exposed at the surface as there is an anticline running roughly north-south along the line of Dovedale. Older rocks are often exposed in anticlines as the higher rocks are stretched and broken during folding. The broken rocks are then easily eroded away, thus bringing the older rocks to the surface.

Photo w8.1

View from summit of Thorpe Cloud towards Bunster Hill, left, and along Dovedale, right.

Another interesting feature is the small dry valley to the north-east of Thorpe Cloud. The dry valley, called Lin Dale, separates Thorpe Cloud from the high point north-east of Hamston Hill. Lin Dale, though now dry, 'drains' towards the north and into Dovedale, rather than to the south and the lower land into which the Dove eventually flows. There is another dry valley to the east of Hamston Hill. The name Thorpe Pasture applies to a wider area than just the valley but, in any event, this dry valley 'drains' south to the lower land.

It is pretty clear that the whole of Dovedale from here to just south of Hartington is an example of 'superimposed' drainage. The theory says that the river course would have been determined long ago when there were overlying rocks, younger than the underlying limestone. No doubt this river course was chosen because the strata on top of the anticline, broken by stretching while being pushed into an upfold, provided the easiest route and much material ready to be carried away. When all the overlying material was removed, the underlying reef and basin limestones were exposed.

Looking back to Bunster Hill the upper slopes seem to dip gently towards the valley before descending, out of sight, precipitously to the valley floor. From the summit of Thorpe Cloud, having taken time to soak up the views if weather permits, head towards the northern end of the summit area to gain a view down into Dovedale.

The rock outcrops on the summit and during the descent contain plenty of fossils, especially brachiopods and stromatolites or fossilised blue-green algae. Take care on the steep descent of Thorpe Cloud's northern ridge as the track can be very slippery. Take time to look at the outcrops that have been polished by countless boots for some marvellous displays of fossils. More fossils including crinoids can be seen in polished rocks at the bottom of Thorpe Cloud just where the stepping stones cross the river (and indeed in the stepping stones themselves).

Follow the main track up the valley, noting that the gap between Thorpe Cloud and Bunster Hill widens immediately after you have passed these two hills, though the valley sides soon narrow in again. After about 450 metres the path starts to rise in steps with laid blocks of sandstones. Many of these blocks also contain plenty of fossils; some well-polished steps display very clear fragments of crinoids, some of which are several centimetres long and 1–2cm wide.

At about 1453 5178, in the vicinity of a striking rock tor known as Lover's Leap, the path rises to its highest point before descending again. On the left of the path there is a small rock outcrop with views into the valley. From the main path look for a small path that goes right up through some trees (just before the main path starts to descend). This small track is marked on the OS map as a series of small black dashes and follows a steep dry valley up towards the stone wall at the top of the valley.

At the top, ignore the footpath signs and follow a small track that bears off left to carry you along the lip of the top of the slope with absolutely tremendous views down into Dovedale's narrowest section. Isolated rock tors can be seen sticking up and out of the mass of vegetation, notably Tissington Spires. Excellent views can be had up Dovedale from some of the headlands that you pass, but also turn round and look back down the valley. From here it looks very much as if Thorpe Cloud and Bunster Hill both slope gently down towards the steep-sided narrow section that now separates them, implying that the valley was originally a shallow-sided affair and has been considerably deepened.

The track carries on for about 1.5 kilometres at roughly the same height offering an excellent high-level traverse (photo w8.2). It passes first around the top of a short, sharp dry valley then drops down and climbs back up across another bigger dry valley before it starts to descend through Upper Taylor's Wood, bringing you back onto the main path just before the caves known as Dove Holes (photo W8.3).

Lower Dovedale

Photo w8.2 | Dovedale in verdant spring garb.

Photo w8.3 | Dove Holes caves.

The caves attract considerable interest from passing walkers. One particularly interesting feature is that the upper right-hand side of the larger of the two entrances displays bedding or layering which shows the way the reef limestone here was built up. Usually reef limestones display little or no signs of bedding, but it can on occasion be seen. Follow the main track upstream for another 250 metres or so until Raven's Tor comes into view on the left-hand side of the valley. The upper right corner of the outcrop also displays some bedding (photo w8.4). This marks the transition from the reef limestone to a 'dark' ramp or basin limestone, which would have been deposited off the edge of the limestone platform. The darkish colour derives from the presence of clay minerals which settled in deepish water.

Continue along the track on the right-hand side of the river, heading towards Milldale. Just before reaching the bridge to the hamlet, bear right on a minor track up to the top of the valley side. Follow the footpath along the top of the valley side with lovely views of the valley ahead. Carry on until you come up to Shining Tor which, if the weather is fine, is an excellent place to sit and study the main valley. Wolfscote Hill, just south of Hartington, can be seen in the distance with a series of intervening headlands; the most prominent is the high point (near Dove Top Farm).

From Shining Tor follow the footpath eastwards for about 300 metres along the top of the unnamed dry valley. At about 1490 5480 a footpath drops down into the valley and down to join Dovedale. At the point where you join the footpath into this dry valley, it is worth noting the valley profile with a gentle slope to the right and a much steeper one to the left. This suggests that the upper part of the valley originally drained into Dovedale at roughly this height, with the steeper section being cut when Dovedale itself was deepened.

Photo w8.4 | Bedding can be seen on the extreme right of the limestone outcrop (ramp limestone), while it is absent from elsewhere in the outcrop (knoll reef limestone).

Follow the footpath down to Dovedale where you join the minor road and cross the river on the road bridge. It is necessary to walk alongside the minor road on a narrow pavement for the next section until reaching Milldale.

The footpath on the right-hand side of the river starts at the southern end of the hamlet just before the bus shelter and information barn (where there is a handy bird's eye drawing of the whole of Dovedale south of Hartington). The entrance to the footpath is narrow and easily missed, so look out for the notice informing you that it is impassable after heavy rain. Note that the impassable section is right at the end of the track before reaching the footbridge near Ilam Rock, so if you take a chance you might have to return to Milldale. Otherwise, while the path is certainly more difficult than the main track, it is not much different from some of the tracks followed on other walks in this book. It can be rather slippery after rain in places.

The track eventually brings you right up under Raven's Tor, where the bedded dark 'basin' limestones can be seen butting up against the reef limestone (photo w8.4). From here you pass back into the reef limestone and the crags and/or steep hillside crowd in on you from the right. After a couple of twists and turns, passing Hall Dale, the crags eventually force you right up to the river (this is the section that becomes impassable when the river rises after heavy rain). Here you will encounter some heavily weathered and lichen-encrusted reef limestone.

Carry on to a footbridge, near where there are impressive views of rock tors. Cross the footbridge to join the main track. Pickering Tor and cave are immediately across the river. The cave is accessible by a short steep ascent on a track.

The next section of Dovedale, from here around Ilam Rock south to Tissington Spires, is one of the narrowest parts of Dovedale (Beresford Dale just south of Hartington may be narrower). Here it truly does deserve the title of a gorge with steep, often vertical, or near vertical craggy sides rising directly from the floor of the valley. Indeed, this section of the valley is so narrow that a wooden walkway had to be built.

Here the river has cut a sharp gorge into the mixed reef and dark basin limestone of this area. The theory is that the river course was determined when the limestone lay under great thicknesses of later rocks. When the river had eroded through these rocks, it was too late to alter the course of the river and it was able to cut down into the limestone while maintaining its course. This is known as 'superimposed' drainage where by down cutting in stages, a more gentle valley is replaced with a deep atmospheric gorge (to the delight of the hundreds of thousands who ramble through it every year).

There is an abundance of impressive rock tors and caves in this section of the walk. One particularly popular feature is Reynard's Cave (photo w8.5). This is a natural arch, presumably originally a cave which was exposed as parts of its surrounding rock were eroded away. The views down the valley from near the arch are outstanding. As you continue along you will see a cave on the left with water running on its floor. On looking into the cave, the water can be seen issuing from near the back. Later on you pass a spring just above the track (just beyond Tissington Spires by a weir and just before a wooden gate). These two water springs must come from caves (perhaps quite small ones) in the rock, but the limestone massed above and around Dovedale is not thought to have any significant cave systems unlike many of the other limestones valleys in the White Peak.

After a short while the track begins to rise slightly, again with stone steps with some very impressive fossils on display. Follow the track to the stepping stones below Thorpe Cloud and, if feasible, cross the river here taking care not to slip as you step across the fossiliferous stones. Then follow the right-hand side track back to the car park/bus stop.

Photo w8.5

Reynard's cave, a natural arch in reef limestone.

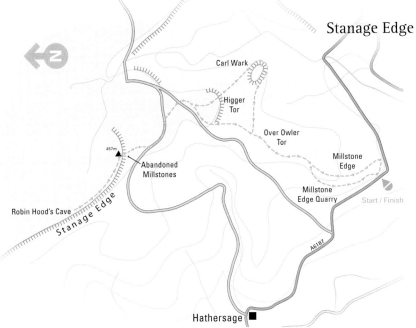

Stanage Edge

Carl Wark

Higger Tor

Over Owler Tor

457m

Abandoned Millstones

Millstone Edge

Millstone Edge Quarry

Start / Finish

Robin Hood's Cave

Stanage Edge

A6187

Hathersage

Walk #9 Stanage Edge

START	▶	MILLSTONE EDGE CAR PARK/BUS STOP (SK 251 801)
FINISH	●	CIRCULAR ROUTE
TIME	◔	3 HOURS+
GRADE	◔	NAVIGATION ● ●
	◔	TERRAIN ● ● ●
	◔	SEVERITY ● ●

This walk, along with walk 10, visits some of the long rocky edges that frame the eastern side of the Peak District. Walk 10 includes Curbar Edge and Baslow Edge, while this walk covers Millstone Edge and Stanage Edge. The walks could be combined or, with the help of the bus, joined into a good long linear walk. On its own walk 9 is a medium-length route, while walk 10 is pretty short. Both walks are accessed from high-level car parks, so that there need be little climbing. This means that there is a very wide range of walks that can be arranged from the two walks to suit many needs, from a very short one (a visit to Curbar Edge or Millstone Edge) to quite a long day.

On both walks the sites of old millstone quarries are passed with finished or semi-finished millstones in places with a particularly good set near the start of Stanage Edge (at about 2505 8295). This walk starts by passing through a line of old quarries (now the lair of rock climbers) ranged out under the eponymous Millstone Edge.

Stanage Edge, Millstone Edge, Curbar Edge and Baslow Edge are all part of the gritty sandstone known to geologists as the Chatsworth Grit. It can be followed as a prominent feature for most of the way from north-east of Dale Dike Reservoir to well south of Baslow Edge (the Chatworth Grit also crops out in the south-west of the Peak District near the Roaches – see walk 11).

The section between Millstone Edge proper and Stanage Edge passes a number of large rocks tors – Over Owler, Carl Wark and Higger Tor. Stanage Edge itself runs on for some distance and walkers are faced with deciding how far along the edge to go before turning round and returning by the same route or by the lower path at the base of the crags.

The views from the edges are very wide-ranging, with overviews of the Peak District hills to the west and open moor slowly fading off into distant urban landscape to the east. To the north and south, the line of moorland continues for as far as the eye can usually see. The eastern views are more monotonous, while those to the west present a varied tapestry of green hills and valleys in complex, intimate patterns. A series of edges on this whole eastern side can be distinguished from some viewpoints as minor upturns on the skyline or intervening high lines, rather like scattered petrified waves.

The rocky edges (and also edges covered in vegetation) are 'scarp' slopes cut down into a layer of sandstone or grit. The area between two roughly parallel edges is known as the 'dip slope' and gives an idea of the extent of any tilt of the beds (due to tectonic collision causing folding in the rocks). It is clearly pretty gentle here, even allowing for the superficial deposits that cover most parts between edges. The scarp and dip slopes are seen in modest-scale version as you approach Over Owler and also Carl Wark.

One feature to keep an eye out for is known as 'cross-bedding', where fast-moving river channels shift position. Cut-off rippled beds from their previous position are seen etched into many of the outcrops on the tops of the edges.

From the car park at the top of Millstone Edge, follow the footpath into the Grey Millstone Quarries below the edge. The path crosses close to a partly made millstone near the exit from the car park (photo w9.1). There are excellent views towards the west over Hathersage to Shatton Moor, with Win Hill in the near distance and Kinder Scout on the skyline. The track then passes a series of quarried areas cut into the Chatsworth Grit with some abandoned millstones: some are finished, some are in progress and one is broken in half.

Photo w9.1
Half-completed millstone,
Millstone Edge quarries.

Further on there is a large horizontal hole near the top of one quarry face (photo w9.2). This is thought to be a 'carbonate conclusion' which has been dissolved away. It formed from an accumulation of plant debris deposited in the sandy bed of a river delta. The patch was cemented together with a calcareous cement (derived from calcite) which has now dissolved on contact with mildly acidic rainwater, leaving this large indentation in the rock face. Such conclusions can be seen on the rocks on this walk and at many different scales from this rather large example to much smaller ones.

Photo w9.2
A large carbonate
conclusion in Millstone
Edge quarries;
see climber upper
right for scale.

Stanage Edge

The quarry faces give a clearer idea of the depth of the sandstone beds here; more of the rock can be seen than on the edges themselves where rock fall and soil formation have cloaked the lower parts of the edges (photo w10.2).

Follow the path that climbs on to the top of the Millstone Edge and turn right for a short distance to appreciate cross-bedding seen in the rocks at the top of the edge. At one point, some beds of thin flaggy sandstones can be seen sandwiched between tougher grits with the overlying beds of grits sticking out above the eroded flaggy sandstones. This is an example of how ice and water erode softer rocks, undermining tougher more resistant ones to create steep slopes (photo w9.3). Ice also gets into any cracks or joints in the sandstone, breaking open the rock as it expands.

Photo w9.3

Thin flaggy sandstones being eroded away underneath sandstone, Curbar Edge.

Having seen enough turn around and head north on one of the tracks worn through the heather. More cross-bedding can be seen throughout the walk on the many outcrops. As well as the details of the rocks, there are the superb wide views now to the eastern as well as the western side. The complicated landscape to the west and north-west is countered to the east by wide open skies. Flattish moorland with occasional edges interrupts the skyline with hints of urban landscapes beyond.

The Chatsworth Grit edge is rather indented immediately north of Millstone Edge and a number of smaller tors with scarp and dip slopes interrupt the view, most noticeably Carl Wark and Higger Tor. The heather landscape is also littered with isolated rocks sculpted into various shapes by wind and sand as well as water and ice. The tracks are sandy because the sandstone has been weathered chemically when exposed to the air and its calcareous cement is dissolved, releasing the individual sand grains from the sandstone. The grains of sand are then whisked up by strong winds which dash them against the exposed rock and carve out shapes thanks to layers of differential strength within the rock. More fascinating examples of cross-bedding can be seen in the tors and individual rocks on Over Owler Tor, Carl Wark (visited on the return leg) and Higger Tor (photo w9.4).

Photo w9.4 |
Cross-bedding, with wind erosion highlighting the bedding lines.

Cross the road at 2560 8227 and again at 2532 8257 and head towards the start of Stanage Edge. Climb up to the trig point and then walk along the edge. Just below the trig point (which is at 2510 8300) there is another collection of abandoned millstones. Make your way along towards Robin Hood's Cave at 2440 8358. The 'cave' (really a collapse in beds of sandstones probably caused by the dissolving away of another carbonate conclusion) is easily missed unless you walk fairly close to the edge of the Edge (photo w9.5). It is found shortly after the Edge flattens out after the gentle drop down from the trig point. The cave allows another view into how the Edges are formed by collapse of lower, weaker strata leaving steep cliffs. Looking south from the area around the cave there is a classic example of the Edge being undermined with most of a rock buttress sticking out above a cleft at its base (photo 6.1).

Photo w9.5 |
Robin Hood's Cave; another carbonate conclusion which has weathered away and caused overlying strata to collapse.

Stanage Edge

From here the Edge can be seen running off to the north into the distance (photo w9.5). It is up to you how far you go but at some point it is necessary to turn round and return. If possible, pick a suitable track to drop down to the bottom of the Edge. Return along the track for a very different view of the rock outcrops and eventually you will pass the collection of unused millstones below the trig point (photo w9.6).

Re-cross the road twice and follow the track up back over Higger Tor to the east of its summit, then aim for the path that runs along the north edge of Carl Wark. Follow that path to the eastern end of Carl Wark (photo w9.7) and then climb up through rock crags to its gently tilting summit plateau. From there walk along the summit plateau to the western end and rejoin the path to the car park, this time keeping to the top of Millstone Edge.

Photo w9.6 |
Abandoned millstones at disused millstone quarry under Stanage Edge.

Photo w9.7 |
Carl Wark, once an iron age 'hill fort' and now a large, isolated tor with its own scarp and dip slope, created by faulting and warping of the Millstone Grit strata in the area between Millstone Edge and Stanage Edge.

Walk #10 Curbar Edge

START	▶	CURBAR EDGE CAR PARK (SK 263 747)
FINISH	●	CIRCULAR ROUTE
TIME	☾	3 HOURS+
GRADE	⌒	NAVIGATION ●
	☁	TERRAIN ● ● ●
	✦	SEVERITY ● ●

For a general introduction to the geology and scenery of the eastern rocky edges see walk 9, with which this walk could be combined (with the help of the OS or Harvey map and use of the bus for one section). This is a very short walk exploring the feel and scale of gritty edge scenery by walking a minor distance out and back along Curbar Edge (or Baslow Edge). It is described as a short-length circular walk or as a link to walk 9. The circular route can be quite wet in the section between Curbar Edge and White Edge.

Curbar Edge

From the car park walk to the start of the footpath along the Edge and then ascend gently to the high point at 2587 7507 to appreciate the wide views and the rocky edge (photos w10.1 and w10.2). To the western side the view is of the limestone plateau and various dry valleys, gorges and quarries carved into it. To the south the rocky edge continues as Baslow Edge, with Gardom's Edge to the south-east and Birchen Edge beyond it (photo w10.2). Curbar and Baslow Edges are part of the Chatsworth Grit, while Gardom's Edge is in the Redmires Flags and Birchen Edge is in the Rough Rock. To the east the landscape rolls off in moorland towards distant urban lands. To the north Curbar Edge runs off into a similar open moorland view.

Photo w10.1 |
Cross-bedding and
undercutting seen
on Curbar Edge.

Photo w10.2 |
Curbar Edge, left; Baslow
Edge, centre right,
with the scarp slope
smothered with rock
fall and vegetation.

A couple of abandoned millstones are soon seen below the Edge, a common sight on the Edges in the Chatsworth Grit and also seen on Baslow (photo 8.2), Curbar, Millstone and Stanage Edges. There are also plenty of very good examples of 'cross-bedding' in sedimentary rocks where one stream channel has cut across another (photo w10.3). A cave, formed by the space left after a carbonate conclusion was weathered away, is also seen just below the Edge some distance along (photo w10.4).

Photo w10.3 |
Cross-bedding in small
tor on Curbar Edge.

Photo w10.4 |
View of Baslow Edge
from inside small cave (a
'carbonate conclusion')
on Curbar Edge

Carry on along the Edge until about 2505 7572 where the Edge starts to descend and the track does a dog leg. Where the track swings sharp left (west) as it descends, break off to the right and follow the narrow track across to the rather inconspicuous rock outcrops of White Edge. The section of moorland between the two Edges can get mighty boggy at times so a loop towards higher ground to the right may be advisable.

Curbar Edge

On reaching White Edge, head for the high point at 366 metres (2605 7643) and carry on for another 125 metres or so until views open up to the north. Having enjoyed the views turn round and follow White Edge south. From here to the trig point at 2638 7585 is a superb but short stride atop a wonderful all-round viewpoint (photo w10.5). White Edge is part of the Redmires Flags, thus forming an edge independently of Curbar Edge. The flags are not as strong as the grits so form a much less prominent feature; however, they have certainly left their mark on the scenery to remind us of the variety of rocky edges, each created by a separate layer of sandstone or grit.

Photo w10.5

White Edge, left, made of a relatively less resistant 'flaggy sandstone', is much more restrained and less rocky than Curbar Edge which is made of highly resistant 'grits'.

From the trig point return towards Curbar Edge and the track to the car park to complete a short circular walk. A visit to Baslow Edge is recommended if time and energy permit for excellent views north to Curbar Edge and to view the south-eastern extension of the edges.

To link up with walk 9, continue north along Curbar Edge ignoring the recommended return route for the short walk via White Edge. Follow the edge north to the road at 2543 7757 then follow footpaths via Hay Wood, Nether Padley and Yanncliff Wood to cross Burbage Brook at 2535 7935. Follow the footpath up to the A6187 at 2490 7995 on the Surprise View bend and to the start of the walk below Millstone Edge among the quarries as described in walk 9.

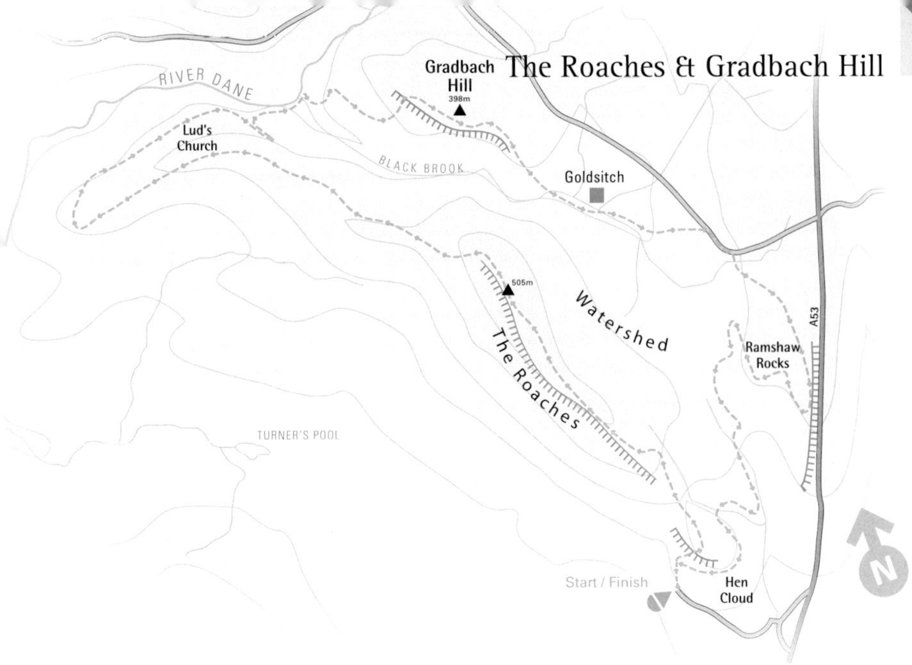

RIVER DANE

Lud's
Church

Gradbach
Hill
398m

BLACK BROOK

Goldsitch

505m

Watershed

The Roaches

Ramshaw
Rocks

A53

TURNER'S POOL

Start / Finish

Hen
Cloud

N

Walk #11
The Roaches & Gradbach Hill

START	▶	FOOTPATH NEAR PADDOCK FARM (SK 0060 6147)
FINISH	●	CIRCULAR ROUTE
TIME	◔	5 HOURS+
GRADE	⌖	NAVIGATION ● ● ● ●
	☁	TERRAIN ● ● ●
	✶	SEVERITY ● ● ●

This walk takes in two of the finest of the Peak District's rocky edges: the Roaches and, with a particularly impressive set of rock sculptures, Ramshaw Rocks. Unlike the long rocky edges seen one after the other on the eastern side of the Peak District (walks 9 and 10) which all face the same way (west), here the situation is different. The Roaches 'scarp' also faces west but that of Ramshaw Rocks, only 1.5 kilometres away, faces east. Each is the classic scarp slope with a gentle 'dip' slope behind, except that here the two dip slopes run into one another and merge in the centre of the valley. These outward-facing scarps are in fact the outward-facing edges of the same bed of gritty sandstone that has been folded into a 'syncline' or downfold. Imagine a slice through a saucer.

In places on this walk the syncline can be seen fairly easily. It is a key structural feature of the geology and landscape of the moorlands of this area and this walk gives a real feel for such a medium-scale landscape feature. The section across the saucer is not quite symmetrical and the Roaches form a distinctly higher ridge in the form of a long, knobbly, rocky crest that dominates the skyline of this south-western region of the Peaks from any viewpoint in the area. This also means that the Roaches ridge is itself a fantastic place for all-round views. Millstone Grit scenery is all around, with the 'steps' in the landscape caused by the interlayering of more resistant sandstone/grit and less resistant shale.

On the microscale, there are fascinating shapes in the rocks produced by the erosion to be appreciated and marvelled at. There are also some unusual examples of 'cross-bedding' where a river channel has left large-scale ripples in a series of beds. The river channel has then shifted position and cut off parts of the old rippled beds, laying new beds at a different angle. On the Roaches there are plenty of outcrops displaying a very regular pattern of cross-bedding.

There is also a landslide which is very difficult to see as it is hidden by trees. However, some of the detail of the landslip can be seen in the form of a very atmospheric cleft (known as Lud's Church) through which you can walk. On the return leg, a small but remarkable example of 'superimposed' drainage where a stream cuts a steep-sided valley through tough sandstone can be observed.

Additionally, this is the only walk in this book which ventures into the small patch of the Coal Measures within the Peak District. Most of the rocks on these western moorlands are Millstone Grit, with lots of sandstone and shale. In the middle of the syncline we find the Coal Measures. The Coal Measures only reach the surface in the area between the Roaches and Ramshaw Rocks, and around the Goyt valley though the rocks are nearly all hidden from view under superficial deposits. The scenery is low-key due to the relatively less resistant nature of the Coal Measures rocks.

Start by going through the gate at 006 615 onto a wide track. After a few metres pick up a narrow track on the right that heads directly up to Hen Cloud, aiming for a gap in the main bastion. At first the track ascends gently but it gets steeper the further up you go and some use of the hands is unavoidable (for an easier route bear left of the crags and follow the dip slope up to the summit). The crags are pretty impressive seen from below and even more so when you consider that the slope up to the base shrouds the lower part of the rock face; they are much bigger than they appear. Follow the track up through the crags, observing some fine cross-bedding on the rocks as you pass through them (photo w11.1). On reaching the summit ridge, turn right to the highest point for superb views all round.

Having feasted your eyes, its time to let them seek out the geological features to the north and north-east. Looking roughly north it is possible to see how the Roaches and Ramshaw Rocks are the twin limbs of a syncline (photo 5.1 and diagram 5.1). What is not obvious is that the long axis of the syncline is not horizontal but plunges to the north. This means that it pinches out on the surface round about where you now stand. In fact, Hen Cloud is where the sandstone outcrops of the Roaches and Ramshaw Rocks meet and form the looped end of the syncline on the surface (see diagram w11.1).

Photo w11.1 | Cross-bedding on the scarp slope of Hen Cloud.

Diagram w11.1 | Geology of the Roaches/ Goldsitch area, showing 'superimposed drainage' of streams cutting channels through tough sandstone.

The Roaches & Gradbach Hill

Looking towards the Roaches edge itself, the 'scarp' and the 'dip' slope are easily seen. Closer examination of the ground to the left of the scarp shows that there is another rocky edge a short distance above the road (photo w11.1). The Roaches (and Hen Cloud and Ramshaw Rocks) are what geologists call the Roaches Grit, but the sandstone of the lower edge is known as the Five Clouds Sandstone. This is a lower (laid down earlier) layer of sandstone, with a layer of shale separating it from the overlying Roaches Grit. To use the saucer analogy, we can perhaps imagine a stack of several saucers with the Roaches Grit saucer at the top and the Five Clouds Sandstone saucer below it.

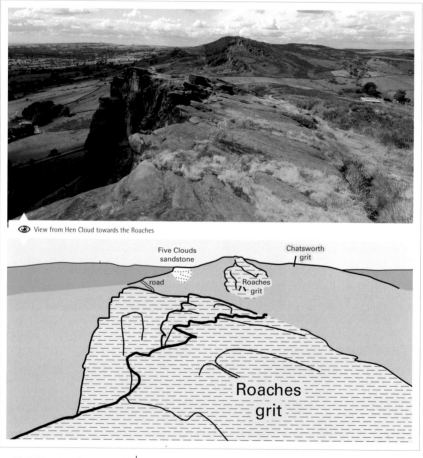

👁 View from Hen Cloud towards the Roaches

Photo w11.2 + diagram w11.2 | The Roaches and neighbouring dip and scarp slopes.

The Roaches & Gradbach Hill

Looking to the right of the Roaches ridge you can see that the dip slope soon flattens out, forming a ledge a short distance below the summit ridge (photo w11.2 and diagram w11.2). Indeed there is even a slight rise to the right side of the ledge. This is another scarp slope (another saucer indeed), a sandstone known as Chatsworth Grit (and which also outcrops on the eastern side of the Peak District). The little headland behind Well Farm is in fact the equivalent point in the syncline in the Chatsworth Grit as Hen Cloud is in the Roaches Grit. The walk eventually returns round the bottom of this small headland.

Not really visible until later in the walk, there are more saucers on top of the Chatsworth Grit. The next saucer up is a sandstone known as the Rough Rock. This is the last sandstone to occur in the Millstone Grit and the rocks underlying the ground behind the ridge (and currently out of view) are part of the overlying Coal Measures (which we can imagine as further saucers on top of the Millstone Grit).

From here we have gained a rough overview of the southern end of the syncline and how it has resulted in the 'saucer topography' described above. For the next 5 kilometres or so the walk runs along the edge of one of the 'saucers'. Here the analogy breaks down and a better approach might be to substitute a stack of guttering, each a little wider than the overlying gutter and the whole stack dipping down in one direction. On this stage of the walk the views of the syncline are generally limited thanks to the gentle dip slope (interrupted as we have seen by the Chatsworth Grit). The Ramshaw Rocks edge can be seen as can edges further north, and there are fine views over Staffordshire and Cheshire to the west as well as along the Roaches edge itself.

Follow the track across to the Roaches and find a suitable route up the crags; the easiest routes involve going to the right and heading up the dip slope. The rock outcrops are worth studying, especially after a couple of hundred metres when they begin to display an unusual form of 'cross-bedding' caused by the shifting of a river channel (photo w11.3). From the regular horizontal beds cutting across dipping beds, we can guess that the shift in the channel happened time and again with the channel appearing to revert to its previous position several times. The horizontal beds may well represent severe flooding conditions, with a temporarily much bigger river channel cutting through a smaller channel.

From near the summit trig point there is a good view of the gentle dip slope down to a wide ledge and a slight rise. This slight rise at the end of the ledge is where the Chatsworth Grit beds lie (diagram w11.1). The Roaches mark the highest point in this area, with lower ground to the west over further lower saucers (older layers of sandstone) and also lower ground to its east over further higher saucers (the Chatsworth Grit, the Rough Rock and the Coal Measures).

Continue roughly north from the summit, taking time to appreciate the wide view over the syncline and beyond. The rocky edge seen due north in the valley to the right is a continuation of the Chatsworth Grit, here forming an edge known as Gradbach Hill (the return route comes along the top of the edge). Here the Chatsworth Grit is no longer a minor ledge just below the Roaches Grit; rather , it forms a fine (albeit minor) edge it its own right.

Beyond Gradbach Hill looking north the central two of the next set of hills have flat summit areas, but there are west-facing edges to the left and east-facing ones to the right. On Gradbach Hill the syncline is quite clear with the flat hills marking its centre. However, the valley between Gradbach Hill and the flat-topped hills marks the line of a fault and the rock outcrops have been shoved upwards and to the left: the Coal Measures no longer come to the surface until further north. The Roaches Grit outcrop curves westwards, forming the curved ridge down from the summit of the Roaches towards the Dane valley as the view ahead shows.

Follow the track down to Roach End where a minor road crosses the route. The walk can be cut short here by following the footpath sign to Lud's Church (another short cut is found further along at about 9875 6520, again with a footpath signpost). The recommended walk carries on over Back Forest to the end of access land at about 9775 6555. The views as the ridge slowly descends and nears the valley of the River Dane are well worth the extra walking.

At 9775 6555 turn very sharp right and follow the footpath to the north-east, eventually swinging east. After a few minutes while passing through an enclosed section, the slope opens out a bit and hummocky ground can be seen: the first evidence of the landslide on the slopes above you to the right. Soon the path enters a well-wooded section and eventually you come to a signpost for Gradbach. On the left are some rock outcrops (to which the route returns after visiting Lud's Church).

Take the (unsigned) minor track above the signpost that heads off right. Follow the track through the wood for about 200 metres until you come across a partially fenced-off tree on the right. Immediately to the right of the fenced-off area is the entrance cleft to Lud's Church. Enter the chasm, descend to its floor and walk through to the far end. The twisting and turning chasm starts off fairly narrow;y, about a metre wide, widens in its middle reaches to about 3 metres before narrowing again. There are several small side chasms (photo w11.4).

Photo w11.4

Lud's Church, a chasm created when the left side slipped away from the hillside on the right, but did not slide any further downhill.

Here you are standing in the gap wrenched into the rocks when the landslide occurred. Had it not been for the woods it would have been possible to see the slipped land below you along the path while approaching Lud's Church. Here the slide has been limited to the space in the chasm between the two rock walls and it has moved only a short distance rather than collapsing and sliding down the hillside.

Photographs of the chasm do not really do it justice, so my comments spoken to my voice recorder on researching this walk and entering the chasm for the first time are worth repeating verbatim: 'Wow. Very impressive, very atmospheric. Overhanging rocks, vertical cliff faces. Dark, dank, the feel of earth movement is palpable. What a place.'

The Roaches & Gradbach Hill

Walk all the way through the chasm and back, returning to the track by the fenced-off tree, then return to the signpost to Gradbach and the rock outcrops. If you climb up on the right of the first outcrop you can see that these are also part of the landslide and have moved much further downhill than at Lud's Church. Follow the track to Gradbach down to the next sign (at the time of writing the sign had fallen over and was propped up against a tree).

Head down to the footbridge (9910 6575) over the stream. Take the right-hand track up towards a farm house (9940 6580), turn right onto the right of way through the farm yard (which turns out to be a store yard for a variety of stonework). Follow the track southwards, past yet more stonework, until you come to a stone wall on the left (9945 6555). Bear sharp left and follow the permissive path to the edge of access land (9955 6558) on Gradbach Hill. Follow the track through heather, bilberry, bramble, bracken, cotton grass and grass up to the ridge line and then turn right to follow the track along the edge towards the summit area.

There are quite good all-round views from here and over the next section of the walk. Different angles on the edges are seen on the eastern side of the area, the flat-topped hills behind and more edges to the west.

Despite the name, Gradbach Hill is another sandstone edge and is part of the Chatsworth Grit. Another edge lies to the left, Middle Edge. This is part of the Rough Rock, the last sandstone layer in the Millstone Grit. Out of sight below Middle Edge are the Coal Measures. The Rough Rock and the Chatsworth Grit both come up from below the Coal Measures on the far side of the valley forming the syncline. The Rough Rock does not really produce any significant edge features, but the Chatsworth Grit rises up to produce a series of tors along the line of its outcrop including Gib Tor (0180 6475) and to its north and south. The eastern line of the Roaches Grit is seen as another series of tors beyond.

Earlier in the walk, from the Roaches, it was seen that the Chatsworth Grit forms a minor rise on a ledge immediately below the Roaches summit ridge. It can now be seen from Gradbach Hill that there is a stream between the Chatsworth Grit and the Roaches Grit.

Once past the highest point it can be seen that the Gradbach Hill grit starts to swing slightly to the right and drop down towards the stream (photo w11.5). It then becomes clear that the ridge rises up the other side of the stream to form the ledge just below the Roaches summit ridge.

The stream rises to the north of the loop of the syncline in the Rough Rock about 2.5 kilometres to the south of the summit of Gradbach Hill. The flattish area around spot height 394 (0125 6285), which is passed later in the walk, forms the watershed. Immediately to the north of the Rough Rock is a layer of sandstone within the Coal Measures. This lies

Photo w11.5 | Gradbach Hill, left, runs down to meet the stream (upper centre) and rises up beyond the stream to form the ledge visible upper right below the summit of the Roaches, extreme upper right

under fairly flattish boggy ground. The stream then starts heading northwards into the lower ground carved into the less resistant shale of the Coal Measures. The line cut by the stream lies in the centre of the syncline.

Instead of continuing northwards along the axis of the syncline, the stream bears progressively north-west to follow the same direction as the Roaches ridge. If we return to the stack of tilted guttering, we can imagine rain falling at the top of pile and running down the centre of the tilted guttering. Imagine, however, that the rain runs down the tilted guttering for a short while but then cuts through one side of the top piece of gutter to run down into the next gutter down.

That is what you can see here as Gradbach Hill descends to the stream but, instead of cutting through a piece of guttering, here it has cut through the Chatsworth Grit. The line of the Chatsworth Grit rising across the other side of the stream is also quite evident, rising to form the ledge and indistinct edge seen from Hen Cloud and the Roaches ridge itself.

The effort involved in carving out this route is evident in the steep valley at the end of the Gradbach Hill ridge, there being a height difference of 50 metres between the stream bed and the highest point. The height difference that would have been cut through if the stream had stayed in the Coal Measures area is just 20 metres, so it would have been a lot easier to have gone that way.

The Roaches & Gradbach Hill

This is an example of 'superimposed' drainage. It is thought that the river course was determined when the whole area was covered by many more beds of sandstone, shale and coal during the time of the Coal Measures, now eroded away. As the stream has cut slowly down, it has maintained its original course. It may well be relevant that a fault line exists (mentioned earlier) running roughly east-west along the Dane Valley. The fault probably played a part in determining the original stream course. This is the most likely explanation of why the stream has suddenly carved a course through the tough sandstones though it may be that glaciers diverted a powerful meltwater channel on to the course of the stream, carving out a course that the smaller present-day stream has kept to.

Shortly you come to a gate on the right, through which you should follow the track towards the stream as the hill declines. For some excellent overviews of the central area, bear left and follow (with a stone wall on the right) the rough track to a pair of gates at about 0053 6500. This is just about on top of the Middle Edge scarp (Rough Rock). The site of Goldsitch Moss colliery is about 500 metres due east of this point (photo 4.1) where the road bends. Coal was dug here from the 15th century through to the 19th. Remains can be seen in the disturbed ground. Each pit represents a shaft dug down into the coal for some distance.

When you've enjoyed the views over the syncline and the shallow area of the Coal Measures, take the right-hand gate and follow over very rough ground to pick up the track from the earlier gate to descend to the stream, meeting it at about 0045 6454, the highest point on a wide track which you meet as you descend into the valley.

Turn left along the track and pass through some sandstone outcrops a bit further on, showing where the stream has cut through the Rough Rock and the Woodhouse Hill Sandstone (part of the Coal Measures). A few outcrops of shale can be seen on the track. An awkward stream/stile crossing marks the end of the sandstone; gently dipping rocks can be seen in the stream side.

Cross the field heading slightly to the left to a gate near a sawmill at Blackbank farm, then turn right back towards the stream and farmhouse. Just before reaching them turn left over a footbridge on to a concessionary path. Once clear of the buildings look around to see the syncline rising on either side from your position in its centre.

Follow the closely fenced path to a stile where outcrops of shale can be seen in the stream side to the right. If you can get a close look you can see an area of slumping (photo w11.6), indicating how shale is friable and easily broken up. It is impossible to get close enough for a good look, but there are clearly dark/black beds within the shales and these may be shale with lots of carbon content or maybe thin seams of coal.

Photo w11.6

Slumping in friable
beds (lamination) of
shale in Coal Measures,
near Goldsitch.

Follow the path to the road at 0167 6380 and turn right along the road. At the road junction at 0182 6355 a choice has to be made about whether to include a diversion to Ramshaw Rocks. If so, follow the footpath heading south-south-east from just beyond the junction. Follow the path all the way to Ramshaw Rocks and enjoy a walk through a gallery of natural sculptures with stunning forms created by sand-blasting (photo 3.7). The sand can be seen on the footpaths. Having been weathered out of the sandstone when exposed to the air, it is then whipped up into a tool by the fierce winds that can blow across the exposed hills. On reaching the road (at 0175 6193 or earlier if preferred) turn right and follow the road to the footpath at the farm at 0166 6257 and turn left. Follow the path down towards the stream to meet a footpath at about 0130 6252 where the routes rejoin.

If you prefer to miss out this diversion, turn right at the road junction and left at the next road junction. At around this second road junction, you can see that the ground is full of low hummocks; these are the remains of the coal mining operations that took place here in connection with Goldsitch Moss colliery. This is also the area just north of the watershed at the southern end of the northwards-plunging syncline. As you go south along the next section of road you will cross the watershed.

Ignore the first footpath you meet on the road, but carry on to the next footpath at 0162 6300 and follow the path down to the stream at 0130 6252 joining the route from Ramshaw Rocks. Here we can see that the watershed has been passed and the stream is flowing south. It has cut through both the Chatsworth Grit and the Roaches Grit just about where they come out onto the surface and loop around.

The Roaches & Gradbach Hill

Follow the footpath south (as the stream cuts through the Chatsworth Grit) to a fording point at 0136 6227 and head uphill and round the base of headland (access land). The stream valley and the headland are where the Chatsworth Grit loops from the north-west to the north-east as it is exposed at the end of the northwards-plunging syncline. When I was here the footpath and access land could only be used by crawling underneath an electric fence (photo 8.4). Follow the path to Well Farm and choose a loop round Hen Cloud either to the south or the north to regain the start point.

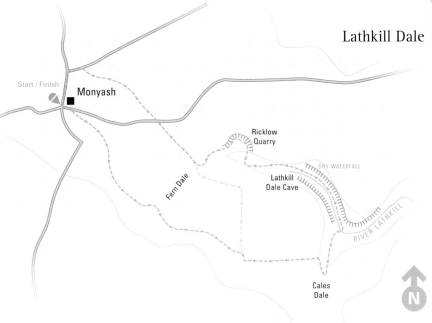

Start / Finish
Monyash
Ricklow
Quarry
DRY WATERFALL
Lathkill
Dale Cave
Fern Dale
RIVER LATHKILL
Cales
Dale
N

Walk #12 Lathkill Dale

START	▶	MONYASH VILLAGE (SK 149 665)
FINISH	●	CIRCULAR ROUTE
TIME	◕	4 HOURS+
GRADE	◉	NAVIGATION ●●
	◔	TERRAIN ●●
	◉	SEVERITY ●●

Lathkill Dale rivals Dovedale in popular affection. From its low-key start as a grassy dry valley (called Bagshaw Dale) just north of the village of Monyash, for the next 9km or so to Alport Lathkill Dale provides stark limestone gorges, stunning wooded valley sides and dark, dank caves where the river emerges. For the walker with an interest in geology the upper sections are the most interesting of all (while offering unrivalled scenic excellence) and this relatively short walk is concentrated around these sections.

Lathkill Dale

This walk starts off in a gentle-sided dry valley, diverts shortly into a fascinating abandoned quarry (the source of very beautiful polished fossiliferous limestone), then into a waterless rocky gorge, past a cave from which the river that flows further down the valley normally flows, then past a 'hanging valley' with a dried-up waterfall, then up a side valley (Cales Dale) and onto the high limestone uplands to return to the start point. The walk could easily be extended by going further along Lathkill Dale to experience the wooded sections of the dale. Unfortunately, there is no easy alternative return route if you do so and it is necessary to return back up Lathkill Dale to Cales Dale to return to the start point.

Ricklow quarry was the source of 'figured marble', which is actually a limestone and not a marble (which is 'metamorphosed' limestone, recrystallised under great heat and pressure). The name 'marble' is often applied to any stone which will 'take a polish' and the highly fossiliferous limestone rocks of Ricklow Quarry do so very well indeed.

After the quarry the attention shifts back to Lathkill Dale, its variable drainage and the varying valley-side forms. This is where the truly beautiful sections of Lathkill Dale begin to take hold of the imagination and invite the visitor to indulge in the sight, smell, taste, sound and touch of the unrestrained scenic charm. Once the walk leaves Cales Dale and climbs up on to the top of the limestone plateau the intimate prettiness of Lathkill Dale is lost, but there are still interesting features to be seen.

The walk starts in Monyash, heading north for some 250 metres from the village crossroads to a road junction. Turn right and almost immediately turn right again on to the right of way into the wide, grassy, dry valley of Bagshaw Dale. The valley becomes almost imperceptibly deeper and less gentle-sided. Increasingly a small section a limestone outcrop becomes apparent on the valley sides.

Shortly, the track crosses a road (B5055). After a while the track approaches the boundary of the land managed by Natural England. On entering the access land area, leave the main track and pick up a track that rises up on the left side of the valley. Follow the path up and, near the top, as it swings left. Some excellent views down Lathkill Dale are to be had from here. Follow the fence down into Ricklow Dale left of the quarry seen ahead (photo w12.1). Head to a gate in the stone wall seen just below you in the dry dale. As you approach the stone wall look for blocks of stone to the right of the gate with amazing displays of fossils.

Photo w12.1

Ricklow Quarry, waste tips built up just in front of the quarry face from which fossiliferous rock was polished as 'figured marble'

Photo w12.2

Ricklow Quarry face, showing bedding, left and top, and waste tip, lower right.

Go through the gate and turn right. More fossiliferous rocks can be seen in the waste tips as you walk through the quarry itself, if you are prepared to take the risk of clambering over the waste tips to get close to the quarry face. Photo w12.2 shows part of the quarry face with three distinct types of bedding and some waste tips in the right foreground. Don't get too close to the quarry face; rock falls obviously do occur here. You can see beds which are made up of packed masses of large fossils known as gigantoproductus and also plenty of crinoid fragments, some up to 2 centimetres or more in diameter (see photo 2.17).

Follow the path through the quarry to meet a stone wall at about 1655 6606 and a set of steeply descending stone steps. Descend into the valley, appreciating the views of the dry, gorge-like section of the dale. On reaching the valley floor, it is worth taking a short diversion by turning right to head briefly up the dale (this short diversion is more easily missed out in summer when the trees are in leaf and little can be seen of the valley sides). The first thing you notice is the great blocks of scree on the right (actually waste tips from the quarry). What is also obvious is that this is a particularly narrow part of the dale, much narrower and more gorge-like than the grassy section met earlier on.

The reason for this sharp and emphatic change in the cross-sectional shape of the valley is that there are some limestone knoll reefs (mud mounds) on either side of the valley. The reefs are more resistant to erosion than the 'shelf limestone' or 'platform limestone' which form the bulk of the rocks here. It is not clear if the reef limestone outcrops on the sides of the valley originally formed one reef and the valley has cut right through, or whether the river was guided into its course by a gap between two separate reefs. This is possibly another example of 'superimposed' drainage, where the river course was set when this whole area was covered by Millstone Grit Group rocks. These were eroded away and the river simply continued to erode down on its same course, regardless of what the underlying geology suggests it should have done.

Most of the limestones seen so far and to be seen further down the dale have more or less horizontal bedding. However, the reefs do show a form of tilted bedding in places, a pattern reflecting stages in development of the reef/mound.

When you have seen enough, turn round and head down the valley. Beyond the stone wall (at the bottom of the steps down from the quarry) you enter a much more open section of the valley and the rocky sides can easily be seen all year round. The pile of rocks on the right is not another quarry waste tip but a natural stone fall when part of the limestone crags came crashing down. The largest blocks built up enough momentum to tumble right into the middle of the dale.

This rock fall is an example on a larger scale of a process which has created the sloping, vegetation-covered, lower valley sides. Material has fallen off the crags, loosened by erosion, and gathered at the base to eventually become covered by vegetation. This can be seen towards the top of the large rock fall where the smaller fragments have gathered and are now covered by vegetation. Lower down, there is currently less vegetation. It will take a much longer time for the lower, larger blocks to become fully covered, but eventually they too will disappear under vegetation, to become just a green bump in the valley side (photo w12.3).

This section of the valley is not lined by reefs, and the limestone crags which can be seen are 'shelf' or 'platform limestone'. Unlike parts of the reefs, these platform limestones are horizontally bedded, indicating the tectonic forces that folded the rocks elsewhere had

Photo w12.3 | Dry gorge cut through limestone. Stone fall on the right.

Photo w12.4 | Lathkill Dale Cave; the river Lathkill emerges from underground here during wet weather but, as shown in this photo, in dry weather the cave dries up.

little effect on these rocks in the middle of the carbonate platform. The tilted beds seen in the reef limestone earlier on was not caused by tectonic pressure, but by the rounded slope of the mud-mound.

This is a highly atmospheric section of Lathkill Dale, the absence of a water course at odds with the obvious water-cut gorge shape of the valley. In hot, sunny weather it can seem as if you are walking down some Mediterranean valley that has lost its river for the summer. In fact, water flows underground in a cave system and in normal weather emerges into the valley at the end of this section from a medium-sized cave on the right (1705 6585); in dry weather even this source may dry up however. If there is no stream issuing from the cave there is little point in exploring it as rock falls near the entrance block the way and it looks as if roof falls continue to take place (photo w12.4).

Almost opposite the cave on the other side of the valley is a small side valley. As you walk past it you can see a 'hanging valley' with a dried up 'waterfall' or rock step across the bedding where a stream used to run (photo w12.5).

Lathkill Dale

Further along the main valley another source of water can sometimes be heard but not seen. The small spring is hidden behind the stone wall on the other side of the river, but in the right conditions it falls noisily into the river. Fossils can be found in the scree in this section of the walk.

Photo w12.5

A 'dry waterfall' draining a 'dry hanging valley'; the main valley has been deepened after the subsidiary valley was excavated.

The described route leaves Lathkill Dale at the footbridge at the end of this section of the dale (at 1743 6546), but you can explore further down Lathkill Dale for the beautifully verdant sections to follow. As noted above, the only feasible return route is to come back the same way when you've seen enough (though a route could be worked out using rights of way on the northern side of the valley from below Mill Farm).

Cross the footbridge into Cales Dale. After about 300 metres follow the track which heads up right towards One Ash Grange Farm. A diversion from here to Arbor Low stone circle is possible by following the Cales Dale footpath via Cales Farm to the minor road, then along the road to the path to Arbor Low via Upper Oldhams Farm.

To continue the recommended route, take the footpath to One Ash Grange Farm. On the way up to the farm you may notice an old lead mine on the left. Continue up to and through the fine old farm buildings. A 'grange' was a farming outpost set up by a medieval monastery. Such farms introduced intensive farming methods but were 'privatised' by Henry VIII following dissolution of the monasteries.

A slight diversion is possible at 1655 6530 to follow a footpath that leads to a section along the southern top of the narrowest part of Lathkill Dale, returning to the route by a permissive path in Fern Dale. Otherwise follow the footpath (marked 'Limestone Way') from One Ash Grange Farm to Monyash.

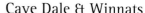

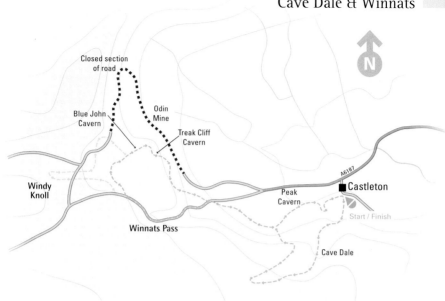

Walk #13 Cave Dale & Winnats

START	▶	CAVE DALE, CASTLETON (SK 1505 8272)
FINISH	●	CIRCULAR ROUTE
TIME	⏱	5 HOURS+
GRADE	◐	NAVIGATION ● ● ●
	◔	TERRAIN ● ●
	◕	SEVERITY ●

Between Mam Tor and just east of Castleton there is a superb set (Winnats, Cave Dale and Pin Dale) of famous incisions into the limestone slope that rises up south of Castleton to form the limestone plateau of the White Peak. Winnats and Cave Dale attract many visitors. Unfortunately (and understandably) fewer trek into Pin Dale.

As well as these three major cuts, there are also some more minor ones (from west to east): Odin Gully separating the Carboniferous Limestone from the Millstone Grit sandstone and shale of Mam Tor; a small 'hanging gully' just to the east of Odin Gully; two narrow insignificant gullies between Winnats and Cave Dale; and the wide, high but shallow area above and around the entrance to Peak Cavern just next to Cave Dale.

Another feature which scars the slope of the limestone plateau is the disturbed ground and a forking mineral vein that rises diagonally up the limestone slope east of Winnats (near one of the 'insignificant' gullies). These etchings break up the otherwise monotonous slope of the edge of the limestone plateau. They allow glimpses into the limestone and allow us to appreciate its complexity and structure.

Here the Carboniferous Limestone was laid down first, forming a 'limestone shelf' or 'platform' on an area of high land. The slope above and around Castleton is where the high (and platform) came to an end, dipping down a 'slope' to a much deeper section of sea bed (a 'basin'). After limestone formation came to an end mineral material carried down rivers was dumped on top, forming an advancing delta. The mud and sand was transformed into the shale and sandstone of the Millstone Grit. These rocks would have covered the entire limestone platform, but have since been eroded away.

Today the Millstone Grit rocks outcrop to the west and north (above the ancient sea basin). To the west on Mam Tor, tough sandstone still stands proud of the limestone plateau. To the north softer shale forms the Hope valley which has been more easily eroded, so that the limestone now stands above the level of the exposed shale. The present-day slope of the limestone platform is actually an exhumed ancient sea bed (which carries on down unseen at the bottom of the present-day slope). Walking through Cave Dale and Winnats thus allows you to travel through slices of a limestone 'apron reef'.

Reefs are complex structures. There is no one simple and obvious type of rock which can be seen and pointed to as 'reef limestone'. Clusters of assorted fossils appear in various places, although in most of the reef exposures few or no fossils are visible (there are however many microscopic fragments). This reflects the varied environment in which the limestone was created. In one area a patch of crinoids may have lived and died; their fragmented remains surviving as observable fossils. In another patch coral may have thrived. Elsewhere the reef environment was dominated by thick mats of blue-green algae where we may find patches of fossilised algae.

It is commonly said that reef limestone is not bedded, but in the walk through

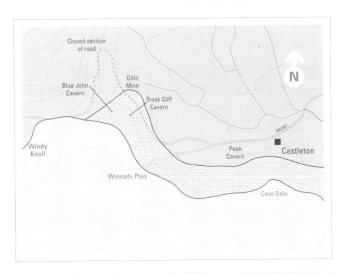

Map w13.1
Geology of
Cave Dale
and Winnats.

shales + sandstones
of the Millstone Grit

platform limestone

reef limestone

Cave Dale it will become obvious that this is not the case as bedding can clearly be seen for some distance up the dale. On entering the dale it is visible in the 'fore-reef' and 'back-reef', effectively layers built up over the reef helping to hold it in place. The limestone laid down behind the reef (the main shelf or platform limestone) was thus protected and not washed away, shielded by the raised lip or rim of the apron reef.

The walk also passes close to several caverns: Blue John Cavern, Treak Cliff Cavern, Speedwell Cavern and Peak Cavern. None are particularly spectacular, least of all Speedwell Cavern, but Blue John and Treak Cliff Caverns have a mass of geological interest and offer a brief trip into the insides of a limestone drainage system. They are part of the scenery of limestone and are well worth a visit.

There are also some volcanic rocks along the way though the outcrops are small and not especially impressive, except perhaps in detail. One exposure of 'basalt' (formed from a flow of molten lava) crosses Cave Dale. The other exposure forms a low, inconspicuous mound at the base of the slope to the east of Winnats and may be a 'vent agglomerate' or an extension of the lava flow which carried on out over the edge of the limestone platform. The walk is arranged so that you climb both Cave Dale (or its lower part) and Winnats. There are two descents across the face of the slope at the edge of the limestone plateau.

Cave Dale & Winnats

Winnats and the area around it are protected as a Site of Special Scientific Interest (SSSI) for geological importance. No samples of rocks or fossils may be removed and there is a hefty fine for transgressors. Pin Dale, on the other hand, is forlorn and unloved; it is effectively out of bounds for walkers. This is because it is a Byway Open to All Traffic (BOAT), open to motorised vehicles which have ripped up the surface to a tremendous extent. The underlying limestone reef geology is the same as around Winnats, where you would get more than a fine if you did this sort of damage.

The path into Cave Dale (signposted from the opposite pavement) looks like a driveway between two houses. The narrow path leads immediately into a narrow limestone gorge with overhanging vegetation, so it is a dark and uninspiring start. From the geological point of view the attention goes immediately to the thin bedding which dips northwards. This non-horizontal dip is not the product of folding caused by continental collision, but represents the original tilt of the beds as laid down on the very front of the limestone reef at the edge of main limestone platform.

What you see on either side at the very start of this walk is a lower part of the front of the reef, the 'fore reef'. The beds are the layers by which the reef was built up, one on top of the other (photo 2.11). Carry on into the dale which soon opens up, widening out to the left and with the tops of the valley sides coming into view first on the left and then on the right. The wider space on the left is the remains of quarrying work. A vertical fault can be seen on the left, and the same fault can also be distinguished behind overhanging vegetation on the right where it includes a small cave. The rocks here contain some fossils, especially to the left. More fossils can be seen in the next headland on the right, with a slippery stony track up to it and back down again (photo 2.10).

The valley then widens out on both sides before narrowing again. Peveril Castle is visible on the upper rim of the left-hand side of the valley. Here bedding is absent or not easy to distinguish, but can be seen in places to be more or less horizontal. The areas where bedding is absent are mainly patches of algal reef poking through the vegetation. This is the central part of the reef. Just before the next choke point a vertical mineral vein can be seen in rocks on both sides but more conspicuously on the left, where there is a remnant of trial mining (photo w13.1). The minerals have been injected into the line of a fault.

The path continues further up the dale with bedding now dipping to the south forming

Photo w13.1 |

There are very few fossils to be seen
in this outcrop, but the line of a fault
and mineral vein is clearly seen where
small holes mark the lower section; the
same fault/mineral vein can be seen
on the opposite side of the valley.

Photo w13.2 |

Outcrop of basaltic
lava on the left of the
track just after passing
through a stone wall.

part of the back-reef area, the opposite direction of dip to the fore-reef. This dip is clearly seen descending down towards a stone wall that crosses the track. Some low-key exposures of a brown rock can be seen on either side the valley just after the stone wall (photo w13.2). This is 'basalt', formed from molten volcanic lava flowing over the limestone platform at a time when it must have been above sea level for a while (as geologists can tell that the lava did not come into contact with sea water). The rock is brown and in places quite crumbly as it is being chemically weathered by exposure to the atmosphere.

Cave Dale & Winnats

Photo w13.3 | Vesicular lava
(outcrop is 50cm across).

Photo w13.4 | Amygdaloidal
lava (width of view 4cm).

On one of the lower outcrops to the right beyond the drinking trough, it is possible to distinguish two micro-features of lava: 'vesicular basalt' (photo w13.3) and 'amygdaloidal basalt' (photo w13.4). A 'vesicle' is simply a fancy name for a little hole and on some of the rocks several such holes, none larger than a pea, can be seen. They are created by gas bubbles escaping from the lava. An 'amygdaloid' is a fancy name for any almond-shaped form and has nothing to do with rocks at all – but it sounds mightily impressive and scientific. What it means in geology is that some of the vesicles can be found filled with calcite, the crystallised form of calcium carbonate. They are a pinkish white colour and about the same size as the vesicles. They are not particularly almond-shaped or easy to find, especially as they are not unlike little patches of light-coloured lichen, so don't worry if you don't see them.

There are very good views down the valley from just before the stone wall and a short distance over to the right (photo w13.5). Return to the stone wall. You can carry on from here for another 400 metres or so within a quite differently shaped valley, now with 'shelf limestone' outcrops above you. The valley gradient is less steep due to the presence of the basalt and the reef limestone forming the narrow point (photo 7.11). At about 142 819, bear sharp right up a track to join the public footpath at about 143 820 which heads towards Peak Cavern.

Alternatively, from the stone wall head up the western side of the valley alongside the old stone wall heading towards Peveril Castle for excellent views back down the valley (cuts out ten to fifteen minutes of walking time). Leave the stone wall at about 148 823 and pick up the public footpath heading towards Peak Cavern, re-joining the main route.

When the footpath bears off right down the slope (towards Peak Cavern), leave it and bear left along another track that descends diagonally across the limestone slope, aiming to meet the footpath and wall at the point where it bends slightly at about 144 825. As you descend note the small wedge-shaped grassy mound to the left of the stone wall. The mound

Photo w13.5 | View down Cave Dale from near the stone wall.

heads up some way into a shallow gully. Another gully is also visible beyond hummocky terrain and a diagonal line climbing up the next section of the limestone slope. Halfway up the slope the line splits into two; these lines are the remnants of lead workings.

The wedge-shaped mound is another outcrop of volcanic rocks; this one is marked on geology maps as 'vent agglomerate' suggesting that it is close to or is an actual volcanic vent. It is also possible that it is an overflow of the lava at the end of the limestone platform. In either case, there is hardly any rock to be seen on the surface and, where it does outcrop, it has been severely affected by chemical weathering. Continue along the path towards Winnats.

Another feature that is not easy to find is what geologists call a 'pebble bed'. These can be found on either side of the opening of Winnats. The outcrop looks like a mass of small, flattish pebbles, but is in fact made up of brachiopod remains. They have been moved around in a strong current and thus are well eroded and unrecognisible. The outcrop on the eastern side of Winnats can be found by leaving the path just before Winnats and looking behind a slight depression at the foot of the lowest part of the slope. Don't worry if you can't find these beds as they don't look very exciting, but they are important as evidence for the view that Winnats is an original channel in the reef along the edge of the limestone platform and not a later valley cut by glacial meltwater (as is thought to be the case with Cave Dale).

Pass Speedwell Cavern (the least interesting of the local show caves) and enter Winnats. Cross the road and walk up the grass into the rocky-sided valley. Although Winnats seems much like the early stages of Cave Dale, it does not turn into a shallow-sided dry valley. These different valley shapes and the existence of the pebble beds support the view that Winnats was present at the time the reef was being developed, not much later as used to be received wisdom. Winnats does not have a dry valley feeding into its upper section. It is now thought

Cave Dale & Winnats

to be a cut through the original reef, creating a channel through which some material could be washed out of the lagoon environment above the limestone shelf or platform.

The outer parts of Winnats, like Cave Dale, represent the fore-reef and there is the same outwards dip to be seen in the thin bedding. Further up the valley it becomes harder to work out the different parts of the reef structure because there are only intermittent outcrops. The reef does not extend as far up the valley as it does in Cave Dale and, shortly after the sharp right bend in the valley, the reef disappears under the main 'shelf limestone' on the left side.

If you have the time it is worth a short diversion to visit Windy Knoll where bitumen can be seen oozing from the rocks near the cave entrance (photo 7.3). Follow the footpath heading north-west from Winnats Head Farm. Dark, sticky-looking substances can be seen on the crags (photo 7.5). The cave entrance is one of a series of features running south-west along the line of streams descending onto the limestone from the impermeable shale to the north-west under Mam Tor and Rushup Edge. From Windy Knoll follow the road to Blue John Cavern.

If you miss out the visit to Windy Knoll, then go through wooden gate on the right at about 132 828 towards the top of Winnats, about 200 metres before Winnats Head Farm. Follow a track roughly north over a slight rise towards Blue John Cavern (1315 8325). The cavern is pretty much devoid of stalagmites and stalactites, but there are plenty of beautiful calcium-carbonate 'petrified waterfalls' to be seen and some small outcrops of the coloured crystal Blue John (photo 5.11). A number of crinoids and other fossils are seen in the cavern walls, as are lumps of chert (formed from silica-rich 'sponges'). Photo 2.8 shows chert nodules in Blue John Cavern; see also photo 2.7 of chert in cuttings into the shelf limestone.

From Blue John Cavern, follow the footpath that traverses below Treak Cliff. The footpath descends into a small dry valley then, at the point where the path reaches the front of the limestone slope, the track bears sharp right. At about this point check the polished stone outcrops in the track for clear examples of fossilised algae ('stromatolites') which were an important component of limestone reefs.

The track leads down to Treak Cliff Cavern which has fine outcrops of veins of Blue John stone (hard to see due to the poor lighting) and some good displays of stalagmites and stalactites, some over 100,000 years old. Follow the track back to the base of the limestone slope. More well-polished rocks in the path show crinoids and other fossils as well as fossilised algae. The path then leads to Castleton where a short diversion is worthwhile to see the impressive limestone crags above the entrance to Peak Cavern. The cave and spring can be seen from the path just before the gate. A tour of the cavern is not of great geological interest compared with Blue John and Treak Cliff, but is of social and historical interest.

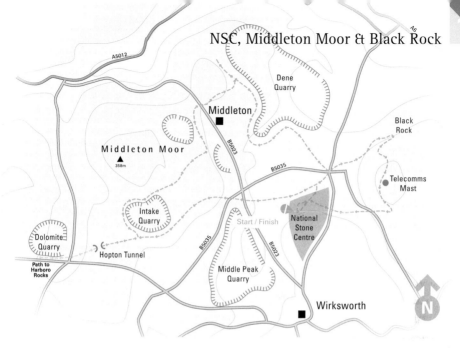

Walk #14 NSC, Middleton Moor & Black Rock

START	▶	NATIONAL STONE CENTRE (SK 288 552)
FINISH	●	CIRCULAR ROUTE
TIME	☾	5 HOURS+
GRADE	☉	NAVIGATION ● ● ●
	☁	TERRAIN ● ●
	⊗	SEVERITY ● ●

This walk goes through, round and past several quarries, old and new, so although rather bleak in places it is interspersed with passages where extensive views can be enjoyed. The quarries are mainly dug into the reef and shelf limestone of the Carboniferous Limestone, though one quarry is seen from which 'dolomite' is recovered. Dolomite is a 'chemically altered' rock which started out as limestone, but has undergone the calcium carbonate being replaced by magnesium carbonate. It is quite common in the south of the White Peak. Geologists are not sure why, when or how this happens, but suspect that 'dolomitisation' would probably have occurred shortly after (a few million years) the creation of the limestone.

The walk starts at the National Stone Centre (NSC) which is situated at the site of an old quarry. There is an exhibition and shop, but the main interest is in the various old quarry faces. Some superb examples of reef limestone fossils are on display including a set of shattered, but fairly complete, crinoids.

There is an interpretation board overlooking the old quarry outside the centre building with a diagram of the whole site. During the 20 years between its opening and my last visit, the area has become covered by tree growth and none of the detail on the board can be seen from the viewpoint (photo w14.1). However, all is not lost and various individual quarry faces can be seen as you walk round the site. A leaflet with some more detail of the geology, ecology and history of the short walk round the centre may be purchased at the shop; my references to location numbers in the walk description are to the numbers in that leaflet (and on interpretation boards).

The walk then passes more disused quarries before circumnavigating part of a large modern quarry where you gain an overview of a noisy, dusty quarry works where big yellow lorries drive up and dump a load of recently quarried boulders into a large chute on their way to be crushed to make road-building aggregate.

There are then some impressive rock outcrops at Black Rock with superb views over the urbanised gorge at Matlock Bath and through woodland, to a high point with views over the urban quarryscape that has intruded deeply into the main limestone plateau in this corner of the Peak District. This walk mixes fine views, fascinating geology and the great scars that mark the importance of the 'extractive industries' to the area's economy.

Starting from the centre building at the NSC, aim for the overview information board to the south-east of the building. At the time of writing trees obscure the view of the quarry as shown on the board, but this may change and the board still offers a useful view of what the area looked like 20 years ago (photo w14.1).

Photo w14.1

Tree growth obscures the overview of the old quarry site at the National Stone Centre, but individual quarry faces and fossils are seen on the route around the site.

From this signboard, turn round and head to the right (east) to NSC trail map location 4. Here there is a small outcrop of limestone with plenty of easily visible fossils, most noticeably large brachiopods known as gigantoproductus. The largest of these shell fossils can reach to more than 10 centimetres across, but there are plenty to be seen here about 7–8 centimetres. Other fossils to be seen in these rocks include crinoid fragments and solitary corals.

Trail map location 5 provides an overview of a disused quarry face (photo 2.3). The rocks here are part of the main 'shelf limestone' and are made up of a limestone mud laid down in beds, one on top of the other on the sea bed in a lagoon. The mud was formed from the smashed up fragments of shells and hard parts of dead animals, excreted pellets and inorganic 'ooids', all rapidly cemented together to form a very tough rock. The beds are fairly thin, just a few centimetres each, though varying in thickness. Throughout the whole section the beds dip very slightly from upper left to lower right.

The beds are also cut through by more or less vertical 'joints', originally developed as minor drying joints soon after the rocks were deposited. These joints are less regular than the bedding, starting and ending, coalescing and separating. The overall effect is to break the rock up into a series of irregular blocks. Some of the bigger vertical joints are faults, created by the tectonic pressures which also tilted the rocks. The bedding, jointing and faulting lines are emphasised by weathering from rainwater which is mildly acidic and works its way into any weakness, accentuating it on exposed surfaces such as this disused quarry face. This is also seen in the quarry floor where jointing and faulting lines can be seen running from the bottom of the quarry face towards your position. At the time of writing, they are increasingly becoming marked lines of vegetation but more general vegetation growth threatens to overwhelm the lines. Photo 2.5 shows a similar situation in an old quarry just to the south-west of the NSC trail (and easily accessed from location 10 below).

Follow the trail south to NSC trail location 6 and a signboard which points out that the lead ore known as 'galena' and crystals of 'baryte' (aka barite) can be seen in the small rock face to the left of the signboard (when facing it). The crystals and metal flecks are most easily seen along the line of a vertical fault on the right side of the rock face nearest the signboard. The galena can only be seen in quite small silver-metallic flecks while the baryte forms small light-brown crystals. This area was widely worked for lead.

Behind a low fence opposite the signboard there is the exposed sloping upper surface of a bed with fragments of crinoids, including a couple of shattered but virtually complete animals. The signboard shows what the living creature would have looked like. Despite its plant-like form, the crinoid was actually an animal and can best be thought of as somewhat like a starfish tethered by one limb, filtering plankton from sea water. The hard parts (rings) which remain as fossils were joined by soft tissue which decomposes quickly after the animal dies, leaving the individual fragments (photo w14.2). Most often you see only mixed up fragments or just a few rings holding together in a short column which have been scattered by tides and currents. Here the animal has fallen to the sea bed where its soft parts decayed but the remaining fragments remained roughly in situ before rapidly being cemented into place by more accumulation of limestone mud. It is from such relatively rare occurrences that geologists are able to reconstruct what such animals would have looked like.

As you follow the path towards NSC trail locations 7 and 8 you pass a series of stone walls made of a variety of British rock types including local sedimentary sandstones, shales

Photo w14.2 |
Crinoid remains in
well-preserved form;
height of image 20cm).

and limestones. Follow the path to NSC trail location 9 for a quarry cut into a limestone 'knoll reef' or 'mud mound'. There is no bedding to be seen at all, except at the top of the far left side of the quarry face (where the top-most bed to be seen is the extension of the crinoid graveyard seen at locality 6). The reef is highly fossiliferous, as can be seen in the rocks that are on the public side of the fence. Some fossilised algal growth colonies can be seen in the main quarry faces.

Follow the path to NSC trail location 10 for a view of the south-eastern quarry which is also cut into a lower part of the same reef complex. Again there is little bedding to be seen except for some gently sloping beds at the very top of the quarry face, some of which have slumped though this is hard to see due to the vegetation. The bedded limestone dips to the right. This represents the way in which these beds were built up over the sloping outer edge of the reef.

The bulk of the face is then made up of reef limestone, though this thins out to the right. Towards the bottom of the quarry face there is a thin bed of volcanic rock which has been chemically weathered into clay. The area to the west of Matlock saw several volcanic eruptions during the period when the limestone was being laid down.

Photo 14.3 | Massive (unbedded) reef limestone topped by bedded limestone, NSC.

NSC, Middleton Moor & Black Rock

From here follow the path back up to the centre building and up the new set of steps, built in a variety of rock types, to the path that goes under the railway bridge. Turn left into the car park and bear left to get onto the railway line, now the High Peaks Trail, and head west. After about 100 metres or so there is a rock outcrop on the left. As you approach it there is a small track that goes off left to the outcrop near a small cave and a fault. Lots of crinoid fossil fragments can be seen in the rock at the western end of the outcrop (leave the path to inspect the rock where it meets the stone wall). As well as masses of piled up crinoid fragments, there are also some large brachiopods (up to 100mm across).

After the trail passes over a road below and then under a bridge, there are outcrops of limestone to be seen on the right with brownish pebbles or larger rocks embedded within it. These 'pebbles' are what geologists call 'chert'. It is very similar to the lumps of flint found in chalk (a very pure form of limestone) and is highly siliceous (high in silica content). Chert is thought to be the remains of clumps of silica-rich sponges that lived on the sea bed, eventually being encompassed within the limestone (photo 2.7).

The trail continues uphill to the steam-powered incline hauling engine at Middleton Top Centre. There are fine views to the south from this high point. Continue westwards along the old railway, at one point crossing a minor road/farm track. The trail passes more outcrops of limestone on the right, bedded and dipping to the right, and with lumps of chert clearly visible. More chert can be seen in the rock exposed by the railway cutting for Hopton Tunnel.

Pass through the tunnel to see dolomitised limestone, which is here a rather dull dark grey (photo 8.3). The recommended route now returns to the minor road/farm track 2710 5477. If you wish to extend the walk for a further 2.5 kilometres to Harboro Rocks, the dolomite there forms impressive rock tors. Dolomite tors are fairly common in this corner of the Peak District where dolomitisation has affected much of the limestone. The impressive rock towers are made up of dolomite which is seen to be full of holes.

Return to the minor road/farm track at 2100 4577 and bear sharp left to follow the farm track to the abandoned farm buildings of Moon Farm. Walk past the decaying buildings to the end and turn right. Note the asbestos walls of the last building on the right and, looking back to the top of the building, asbestos roofing. After passing through a gate bear sharp right at a footpath sign, and head up with the wire fence to your right. The disused Intake Quarry is largely out of view to the right but it becomes increasingly clear that the path is running between the fenced-off quarry workings to the right and the remains of much older mining works to the left, in the form of slight hummocks and pits. These are the remains of mineral mining, not limestone quarrying.

From the rounded summit it is worth taking a look at what can be seen of the upper parts of the quarry face of Intake Quarry. The face looks very much like the bedded limestone seen in the quarry faces earlier on in the walk and on other walks in this book. In places, you can see the thin bedding on the upper face and much thicker beds ('massive' in the geological jargon) in the lower section. However, if you turn round and look back in the direction from which you have just come, you will see another quarry (marked just as 'works' on the OS map at 260 546). This quarry is in the dolomite area and the rocks are a reddish-brown colour, quite different from the limestone in Intake Quarry. There are also superb views here south to the Midlands.

Carry on heading roughly north-east on the footpath, past a covered mine shaft and other workings. After passing through a second stone wall and approaching a third with a clump of trees on the left, more mining hummocks can be seen to the right. Further on to the left, some old mining buildings and another capped-off mineshaft are visible.

Follow the footpath as it becomes a lane enclosed by stone walls. You soon pass the top of an old quarry on the left with formidable-looking fence, sensors, CCTV and stern warning notices. You are informed that it is an 'experimental test site'. Naturally, it is not considered important to inform the passer-by what sort of experimentation is going on or for whom. You are however told that the CCTV is linked to the police control centre. These strenuous measures seem designed simply to keep people away from the top of the old quarry face as, lower down it is easy to wander into the quarry itself.

Follow the footpath down to where it turns sharp left. There is a handy bench where you can sit in comfort with superb views over Middleton and beyond to Black Rock on the right and Masson Hill on the left. All the vegetation-covered ground to the right and below and to the left is disused quarry workings. Follow the lane to where it turns sharp right (at 2743 5650) down into the village. Cross the road and follow the minor road north-east to 2793 5636 and turn sharp right, following the footpath to the edge of Dene Quarry occupying Dean Hollow.

For some reason quarry operators like to top their quarry faces with a dump of material which screens the quarry from view. To get the best view of the extent of the quarry it is best to turn left and head 300 metres north to the corner of the quarry. Otherwise, turn right and follow the footpath round the perimeter of the quarry with the odd glimpse into its deep workings. Although it is hard to get to see the quarry faces in detail, you are provided with full-on views of the quarry crusher workings towards the southern end of the quarry. However, it is difficult to judge the full extent of the quarry itself from this viewpoint (photo 8.1).

Just at the end of the area where you get the views of the quarry works, there is a small outcrop to the left of the path with fossiliferous limestone to be seen. Carry on along the

NSC, Middleton Moor & Black Rock

footpath, passing more old mine hummocks, leaving the perimeter footpath at 2872 5575 and following a footpath south-east heading towards Steeple Grange. Cross a minor track and follow the footpath through a small industrial estate to the main road at 2892 5564. Cross the road with care and follow a footpath to a minor tarmac road; turn right onto this minor road and then left onto the High Peaks Trail. Follow the trail looking for track heading up right to Black Rock (near the end of the car park on the left side of the trail).

The 'dip' slope is to the right and the 'scarp' slope to the left. In front of the rock outcrop of Black Rock is a slope of small stones. This is a waste tip from lead mining here in the 19th century when a shaft was sunk to a depth of 128 metres. Head round the waste tip to the back of Black Rock and to the top for super views towards the Matlock gorge, cut through limestone, and Masson Hill, made of volcanic rock and dolomite (photo w14.3).

Photo w14.4

View from Black Rock, foreground, to Matlock gorge, centre distance, Masson Hill upper left.

Drop down from the top of the rocks to pick up a track that goes down right and then bends left to climb up through the woods. The path eventually leads to the top of the hill near the radio transmitter mast. The top is less densely wooded and is covered by heather and moorland plants, such a contrast with the grassy hills of the limestone plateau. From near here there are excellent views over the National Stone Centre below and many of the quarries.

Follow the path through a gate well to the right of the transmitter mast. The path leads you down to a minor road at 2942 5507. Turn right along the road for 100 metres and then turn left onto the footpath. Follow the footpath to a minor lane, turn right and right again and at the next junction turn left to get to the main road at 2892 5510. Cross the main road with care and take the footpath which leads you into the south-eastern end of the National Stone Centre.

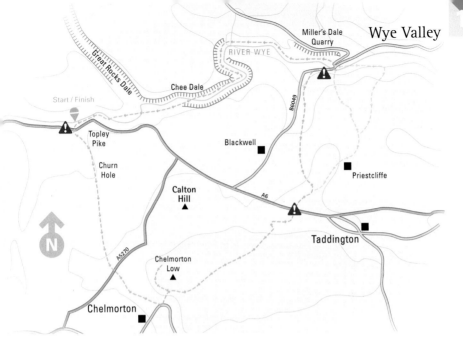

Walk #15 Wye Valley

START	▶	A6 CAR PARK/BUS STOP (SK 103 724)
FINISH	●	CIRCULAR ROUTE
TIME	⏱	5 HOURS+
GRADE	⊙	NAVIGATION ● ● ●
	☁	TERRAIN ● ●
	⊗	SEVERITY ● ● (+DANGER AT TWO ROAD CROSSINGS)

The Wye Valley is understandably one of the most popular parts of the Peak District. From Buxton to Bakewell it is a beautiful scenic gem, twisting and turning like a piece of string. The hard part is choosing which section of the valley to include, there are so many fine examples to choose from.

For many, the section of the trail between Deepdale and Cressbrook is the most magnificent. For this walk I have however chosen one of my favourite sections of the

Wye Valley

valley between Topley Pike and Miller's Dale, including the impressive gorge around Chee Dale. Here the river has cut deeply into the limestone to create vertical to over-hanging walls for a good section of the walk.

The recommended route also crosses part of the limestone plateau and follows a route over hills underlain by volcanic rocks. This medium-length walk provides a scenic overview of the variety of the White Peak's limestone scenery and its subtle modification by volcanic action.

The walk starts with a bit of industrial desolation that rapidly turns into a small gorge with an even smaller upper gorge with a cave entrance, Churn Hole, before rising into a classic gentle, limestone dry valley. This leads you over limestone plateau farmland, framed by low hills that rise above the surrounding limestone due to the strong volcanic rocks that underlie them. Though nearly all covered by vegetation, an outcrop of basalt lava is passed at one stage on the walk. At one point an optional diversion takes you to the top of Chelmorton Low (a hill despite its name) with fan-tastic views all around. The walk then descends bit by bit into the luscious Wye Valley, visiting an old quarry, then heading straight into the Chee Dale gorge and a fitting finale to the walk.

Over a modest distance, the walk covers many of the main features of the White Peak landscape from the rolling limestone plateau, dry valleys, springs, deep valleys, gorges, volcanic rocks, quarries and human communications links (parts of the walk make use of minor roads and an old railway line). It also passes small villages and isolated farmhouses. If you want a short introduction to the components of White Peak scenery this walk is ideal.

There are two words of warning, both involving roads and motor traffic. First, the walk is described as following an anti-clockwise route with the intention of finishing with the stunning trail through the Chee Dale gorge, surely the highlight of the walk. However, this means that the A6 has to be crossed on the inside of a bend where it is impossible to see traffic coming from more than a few score of metres. This means it is essential to cross only when you can hear no traffic from either direction. To avoid this danger the walk can be done in the reverse direction. This would mean that the road is crossed at the end of the day on the outside of the bend where there is better visibility, but it does mean that the most beautiful part of the walk comes at the beginning. Second, the recommended route includes a short section (about 350 metres) along the B6049 near Miller's Dale. This road is quite busy despite being a B-road, with the traffic including large lorries; there is no adequate pavement or verge to walk on in places and so great care needs to be taken here. This section can be avoided by extending the walk as described below.

From the car park, cross the road with very great care. The footpath is on the left side of the quarry entrance road, behind a wooden fence. In summer the path gets fairly overgrown and it may be necessary to squeeze into a narrow space between the wooden fence and the vegetation. The limestone is well exposed in the cutting to the right. Some fossils can be seen in the limestone outcrop on the left as you near the quarry entrance. The next section, alongside an unpleasant pool of industrial waste water, is soon over and you start to enter a widening limestone valley.

After about 300 metres you come to a junction of valleys and a signpost. The right-hand track heads into the main valley, Deep Dale, but the recommended route keeps straight ahead (signed Chelmorton) entering a small side valley that rapidly narrows into a gorge. At some point or other it is necessary to cross the tumbled-down stone wall and the track then heads up towards crags on the right-hand side of the narrowing gorge. A cave entrance, Churn Hole itself, can be seen on the left-hand side as the track swings right.

In summer with thick vegetation it looks as if you are heading into a dense and impenetrable thicket of greenery with no apparent way out. Stick with the track which leads you up into a higher, smaller, narrower gorge, rather like a miniature version of the first part of the gorge. The upper gorge is very short and you are led up to a stile leading into a gently-sided, gently-dipping dry valley. Follow the path up the centre of the dry valley. After about 250 metres and crossing a fence and then an old stone wall, you pass the line of a mineral rake crossing your route, recognisable from the small pits and mounds. As you go up the valley you get better views to the left of the line of volcanic hills. Calton Hill is just about seen but Chelmorton is quite conspicuous.

Follow the path to a road and cross it to enter a track heading south-east towards Chelmorton. After about 150 metres the path moves slightly away from the stone wall on the left and there is a triangular patch of rough grass between the track and the wall. This is where an underlying patch of 'basalt' (solidified lava) fizzles out. Nothing of the rock is seen

Wye Valley

here, but a small disturbance in the land can be seen heading north-west from here. This is just about discernible and adds nothing to the scenery.

However, another stretch of basalt runs along the bottom of Chelmorton Low. The hill, which reaches 446 metres, is highly conspicuous from here (in part because it has been vandalised by massive graffiti cut into the vegetation). The basaltic rocks then swing right to form the slope behind Chelmorton, most noticeably as Nether Low which tops 400 metres. In fact the basaltic rocks extend for another 2 kilometres south of Nether Low, forming a line of hills including Great Low where the basaltic hills die away. More such distinctive hills, marking the line of basalt rocks, are seen later in the walk near Taddington and Priestcliffe.

Volcanic eruptions affected the eastern and south-eastern parts of the White Peak during the Carboniferous Period while the limestone was being laid down. It is known that the volcanic rocks around here are those produced by 'basaltic' lava flows over land, so these eruptions must have occurred at a time when the top of the limestone was temporarily above sea level (due to a drop in sea level caused by an intensification of glaciation and/or intermittent interruptions to the steady subsidence needed for more and more sedimentary rocks, such as limestone, to accumulate). The extent of the present-day outcrops of the lava indicates that there were several episodes of eruption and that the flows were quite extensive, covering a wide area.

The volcanic rocks in the Peak District are not exposed on the surface to any great extent, nor have they had such a conspicuous effect on the scenery as the volcanic rocks of the Lake District or Snowdonia. However, these rocks have scratched a more subtle signature in the scenery such as these minor hills rising up from the rolling limestone plateau in a distinct step. This walk traces few such soft features, but there are many more in the White Peak easily visible to the attentive walker equipped with a geology map as well as a topographical one.

When you reach the village of Chelmorton, turn left on to a minor road for just over 100 metres until you arrive at the bottom of Chelmorton Low. The recommended route takes a short diversion to go to the top of Chelmorton Low and back down again. If you wish to miss this out jump to the end of the next paragraph; otherwise, bear left through the gate onto access land.

The path zigzags up the steep lower slope, but you can choose you own way up. Because of a fault zone the basalt here has been shoved by tectonic forces to the west, so here you are crossing limestone all the way to the summit (unless you go on to the west-facing flank of Chelmorton Low, but this is pretty steep and rough). Climbing up directly on the southern flank takes you across the line of a mineral rake and workings. Continue to the summit for excellent all-round views of the rolling limestone plateau and the intruding volcanic hills. If you do have a geology map, this is the place to trace the scenic contribution of the ancient volcanic lava flows. Though the basalt rocks do give rise to higher points, it is also true that some of the high points seen from here are limestone and not basalt so it would be a mistake to conclude that all high points must be volcanic. The contribution of volcanic rocks is local and needs care to discern, but once identified it becomes fairly obvious.

Return to the access land gate and bear left to follow the bridleway heading north-east. Just to the left as you start heading up there is a signboard with information about the spring here. This spring is at the junction of the impermeable basalt (the section which has been thrust westwards) and the limestone above. Water permeating through the limestone comes to the surface when it meets the basalt.

Follow the footpath uphill. Where it splits, take the left-hand track with a ditch between the two tracks: the same mineral rake as just seen on Chelmorton Low. The footpath follows close to the line of the worked rake, known as Grove Rake, for the next 2 kilometres. The right of way passes through Fivewells Farm , although I experienced some difficulty when I was last there due to a couple of partially blocked gates and an electric fence strung across the way which has to be squeezed under. However, the route of the right of way is clearly marked on the OS map and can be followed, with a little determination, to a footpath sign at 1285 7105. The alternative is to run a little dog leg using the footpath from Pillwell Lane to Sough Lane and rejoin the recommended route at 1285 7105.

This brings you out on top of a north-facing slope with fantastic views of the hills and undulations of the landscape in front of you. The slope is underlain by more basalt, the same outcrop that buttresses Chelmorton Low and Nether Low. The same outcrop can also be seen in Priestcliffe hill a kilometre to the north-east.

In the area at the start of the downwards slope more mineral workings can be seen, again on the line of the same mineral rake. Drop down the top part of the slope to the gate at 1291 7111, either directly or via the zigzag track, and go through a gate to follow the walled lane (ignoring the footpath sign pointing roughly north). About 20 metres after going through the gate, you come across some dark rock outcrops under-foot and on the sides of the track (at the time of writing, under a maple tree). In places there are lots of small holes on this black rock (an outcrop of basalt). The small holes are gas escape bubbles and are known as vesicles, so giving us 'vesicular basalt' or 'vesicular lava'. This is an indication that the lava was erupted and deposited on land. Lava erupted or deposited under sea looks very different. It from such observations and analysis that geologists are able to work out that the limestone area was thrust above sea level several times. This is the first time on the walk that the basaltic lava has been exposed on the surface, though we have seen that it has had a slight effect on the scenery.

Photo w15.1 | Sough Top: a low line of hills formed by volcanic rocks rising up above the limestone.

Follow the track down towards the main road, turning to look at the basalt slope (photo w15.1). Similarly, the hills on the right around Priestcliffe are also volcanic features. Cross the main A6 road very carefully. Follow the minor road for about 300 metres and then turn left. If you wish to extend the walk and/or avoid the section on the B6049 do not turn left here but carry on to 1440 7212 and follow the lane northwards. Either follow this lane to 1390 7260. Take the footpath to Miller's Dale and rejoin the main route or take the north-east heading footpath from 1400 7220 to join the old railway track in the Wye Valley at 1430 7250.

On the main route, follow the minor road for about 125 metres before leaving to continue straight along 'Long Lane' which runs down towards the Wye Valley. After a while the lane swings right and some excellent views of Blackwell Dale and the Wye Valley are on offer. A particularly noticeable feature is Knot Low on the northern side of the Wye Walley, formed of more basaltic lava. The lava outcrop continues to run north and then north-west from here and is joined by more outcrops to the north-east and south-west. The lava also runs to the east along the southern side of the Wye Valley from here, helping form the steep slopes above that section of the valley.

On meeting the road, conditions seem marginally preferable on the left-hand side as there is more visibility being on the outer side of the bend, but take great care. Gratefully reach the pavement at the bridge, cross it and bear left through the gate and ascend the steps to join the Monsal Dale Trail on the line of an old railway.

Head west along the old railway track for a short distance. After passing a signboard, pick up a minor track to the right which leads off towards the disused Miller's Dale Quarry.

Locate a stile in the south-western corner of the quarry area and follow a narrow track back to the old railway line and turn right to continue west. Very shortly you approach a bridge taking the old railway line across the river. Walk out onto the bridge for views then return to its eastern end and descend steep steps (with crinoid fossils visible in the rocks in the steps) taking you down to the floor of the valley. Follow the path along the bottom of the valley. After about 75 metres or so the valley is underlain by more basaltic lava as an outcrop crosses the valley floor. The basalt comes to the surface for about 200 metres and can be seen in some places. The basalt ends where a stream surfaces at the base of some crags. The spring occurs here as water permeating the limestone is forced to the surface as it meets the impermeable basalt.

From here on it is possible that the main track will be impassable in a few places following heavy rain. The alternative route misses out all the wonder of the gorge in Chee Dale, so aim to avoid this walk in very wet weather.

Follow the track into the increasingly narrow and high-sided valley. The route needs no specific instructions except to point out that, in sections, the gorge is so narrow that there is no room for a path at the bottom of the gorge sides; stone steps have therefore been placed strategically along the route.

The gorge becomes deeper, narrower and steep-sided. You may come across climbers tackling the steep crags; indeed, they can often be seen where the crags are overhanging (photos 7.12, w15.2 and w15.3). In such sections you can see how the gorge has been created by the powerful river flow in flood conditions. Boulders are slowly carried down undermining the cliffs at river level until the mechanical strength which holds the rock together is overcome by gravity and the overhang collapses. Clearly limestone is an immensely strong rock (thanks to its naturally powerful cement) to produce such vertical or over-vertical cliffs. However, it is also susceptible to being dissolved by rainwater. The big tough kid has its tender spots, but here it is all brash youthful confidence. The gorge becomes more and more impressive as you go on (crossing the river as necessary on footbridges).

The Wye rises near Buxton to the west and cuts across the limestone plateau to join the

Wye Valley

Derwent near Rowsley in the Millstone Grit. The Derwent then flows south and, near Matlock, leaves the Millstone Grit temporarily to cut another gorge through the Carboniferous Limestone before again flowing over the Millstone Grit south of Matlock Bath. These gorges are examples of 'superimposed' drainage. There are other examples in the White Peak, such as Dovedale, and it is a common feature of the area producing some stunning scenery.

The Chee Dale gorge is surely the most stunning example of such a gorge. The theory is that the river's course had been determined in earlier times when the limestone would have been buried under later sediments of sand and mud creating the Millstone Grit (and probably also Coal Measures and later rocks). These overlying rocks have been eroded away, but slowly enough for the river to maintain its existing course and cut down into the tough limestone as it was uncovered. No doubt there is a gorge in this section of the valley because of the band of hard volcanic rock downstream which forced the river to cut a narrow channel.

Photo w15.4 | Looking downstream towards the start of the Chee Dale gorge.

Wye Valley

Another cause of superimposed drainage can be when the land is undergoing sustained, slow uplift (such as what happens when tectonic plates collide over long periods of time). Under such conditions a river can cut down into the bedrock as quickly as it is being uplifted, thus maintaining its course. This could have happened here as this section of the river cuts through the core of the major anticline shaping the Peak District limestone plateau. This anticline would have been pushed up only very slowly by tectonic forces, so could account for the dramatic gorge. It seems unlikely, however, that the river could have maintained its course over such a very long period of time and this is probably not what caused the superimposition of drainage here.

This section of the walk is probably the most visually engaging and geologically impressive example of a gorge cut by superimposed drainage in the Peak District. It should be taken slowly and enjoyed for its sublime natural beauty, for shortly the walk must re-join the old railway track and then a rough vehicle track back to the start point.

Acknowledgements

My thanks to David Evans, Antony Brian, Vaughan Thomas and Emma Williams who have read and commented on parts of the draft. Albert Benghiat kindly led me on a walk in the Castleton area, allowing me to benefit greatly from his experience of undertaking geological mapping in the area. Jill and Albert Benghiat gave me a warm welcome when I chanced upon their admirable GeoHut (see page 88). Clair Drew and Reg Atherton acted as 'guinea pigs' for some of the walks. Franco Ferrero and Peter Wood at Pesda Press continue to provide enthusiastic support for the third book in the Rock Trails series. Thanks to Peter Grace of White Spider Books, Caernarfon, for suggesting this book. My thanks to Hulme End campsite and Pindale campsite for providing good, reasonably-priced camping accommodation during my field researches. Also thanks to Don at Bute Cartographics.

Bibliography

N Aikenhead, *British Regional Geology: The Pennines and Adjacent Areas*, Nottingham 2002

T Brighton, *The Discovery of the Peak District*, Chichester 2004

F Broadhurst, *Rocky Rambles in the Peak District*, Wilmslow 2001

F W Cope, *Geology Explained in the Peak District*, Cromford 1998

R Dalton et al *Classic Landforms of the Dark Peak*, Sheffield 1990

R Dalton et al, *Classic Landforms of the White Peak*, Sheffield 1990

T D Ford, *The Castleton Area*, Derbyshire, London 1996

T D Ford, *Rocks and Scenery of the Peak District*, Ashbourne, 2002

R Millward and A Robinson, *Upland Britain*, Newton Abbot 1980

M Shoard, *A Right to Roam*, Oxford 1999

R Solnit, *Wanderlust: A History of Walking*, London 2002

P Stanier, *Stone Quarry Landscape: The Industrial Archeology of Quarrying*, Stroud 2000

C Waters et al, *A Lithostratigraphical Framework for the Carboniferous Successions of Southern Great Britain (Onshore)*, British Geological Survey Research Report, RR/09/01, 2009 (www.bgs.ac.uk/downloads/)

C Waters et al, *Lithostratigraphical Framework for the Carboniferous Successions of Great Britain (Onshore)*, British Geological Survey Research Report, RR/07/01, 2007 (www.bgs.ac.uk/downloads/)

E Wood, *The South-West Peak: History of the Landscape*, Ashbourne 2007

Geologese

The language of geology is central to its scientific methodology, but it all too easily acts as a barrier to a wider understanding of the subject. 'Geologese' is confused and confusing. For example **dolomite** and **dolerite** both occur in the Peak District. They sound very similar but are fundamentally different types of rock. Dolomite is chemically altered limestone (magnesium carbonate replacing the calcium carbonate), while dolerite is an igneous rock (intrusive basaltic). Geologese is also forever changing and at a rate which only professional geologists can keep up with.

The divisions of the **Carboniferous period** which I have used in this book are the traditional ones, used in generations of guidebooks and textbooks. However they are no longer current (due to more precise analysis of the Carboniferous period rock strata in Europe). Thus the Carboniferous Limestone is now referred to as the **Dinantian**, the Millstone Grit as the **Namurian** and the Coal Measures as the **Westphalian**. The concordance is not as precise as this implies (the older divisions being based on analysis of the rock 'lithology' and the newer ones on fossil analysis). However, even these names are now being discouraged in favour of names used for Carboniferous period rocks in the USA. Rather than try to keep up with the latest terms, I decided to stick with the familiar names.

Geologists are able to correlate Carboniferous period limestones, sandstones, grits, shales and coal seams in other parts of Britain (such as Scotland and Wales) – and in other countries (such as Ireland, Belgium and Germany) – with those in the Pennines as they often contain the same types of fossils. They can also differentiate the limestones of the Pennines from, say, limestones found elsewhere in Britain from a later geological period (such as the 'Jurassic period' when the limestones of the Cotswolds were laid down).

The traditional names are not ideal. In the chapters on the **Carboniferous Limestone**, **Millstone Grit** and **Coal Measures** (chapters 2, 3 and 4, respectively) – I outlined why each name is confusing or misleading. However, despite their limitations they convey more about the rocks (limestone, grit and coal at least) than Belgian or German place names.

I have also ignored another big ongoing name change. This one involves setting up a new and hopefully more coherent system of classifying rocks. When it comes about it will no doubt be better than the present more or less haphazard system that has accrued over the years. Better techniques of analysis of rocks have highlighted many inconsistencies with the present naming system, so such change is necessary. However, once again it would be confusing to jettison long-standing and familiar names.

In the past **coarse sandstone** (i.e. one made of large grains of sand) was called a **grit**, but this name is now officially out of fashion with geologists. However, the name is so widely and appropriately used that it would be silly to try and expunge it from a (hopefully) popular guide to the group of rocks still officially called the Millstone Grit for some purposes (and the Namurian for others).

The term **shale** is also currently being expunged from the geological literature, to be replaced by **claystone** (which also refers to what used to be called **mudstone**). Again it would be foolish to give up use of shale when all previous popular guides have used the old name. It would also put us in the awkward position, for example, of having a rock formation called the Edale Shales consisting of claystones rather than shales. The case of shale shows up some of the limitations of the new system. Shale is very distinctive: dark or black, laminated and easily friable. Mudstone is dark or black, but crucially lacking lamination and not very friable. But both would be claystone under the new system. The system allows for qualifiers, so one could refer to 'friable, laminated claystone' to distinguish it from 'hard, massive claystone', but this complicates the matter and will introduce inconsistencies with one writer using the naked label and another dressing it up with qualifiers.

Geology students should ignore my example when writing essays but, for the rest of us, let's hope that grit and shale are both highly resistant names and survive for a long time, whatever their comparative lithological resistance to erosion!

Another problem is the superfluity of names for some features. **Knoll reefs** are also sometimes known as **reef knolls, mud-mounds, bio-herms** and **Waulsortian banks**. Actually, the prosaic mud-mound label, though not so exotic as knoll reef or Waulsortian bank, is the most useful name as they are indeed mounds of limestone mud. **Apron reefs** are sometimes known as **Cracoan reefs** (which sounds as if it is named after some distant exotic atoll, but is actually derived from a village in the South Yorkshire Dales overlooked by such reefs). Some geologists don't recognise the idea of an apron reef at all, concentrating on different aspects such as the **fore-reef, algal reef** and **back-reef** distinguishable in places such as Winnats and Cave Dale.

I have treated one geological term with deliberate disregard. **Outcrop** is strictly speaking the whole area where a rock type reaches the surface, whether it is exposed to view or not. When a rock is covered by soil, alluvium, peat, etc, it is still an outcrop. This conflicts with everyday understanding of the term and I have used it in the popular sense to mean a rock that is visible at the surface; an **exposure** means the same. The geologically proper meaning of outcrop is covered by another term: **bedrock**.

Glossary

Algae – micro-organisms. One of the oldest forms of life on earth; blue-green algae live in colonies which secrete a carbonate mat which can survive as fossils (see 'stromatolite').

Apron reef limestone – 'limestone' laid down on the rim of a 'limestone platform'. Often consists of a 'fore-reef' and a 'back-reef' as well as other sub-sections.

Back-reef – 'reef limestone' laid down, often with thin bedding that dips down towards the centre of the 'limestone platform'. See 'apron reef limestone'.

Basalt – rocks formed from 'basaltic' lava flows.

Basaltic – describes the chemical nature of molten magma as low in silica content (contrasted with rhyolitic which is high in silica content); cools to form 'basalt' if it flows onto the surface as lava, and as 'dolerite' if it doesn't reach the surface and cools down below ground.

Basin – low-lying area (usually but not necessarily under sea level) – of basement or present-day surface. Rivers drain into basins and sediments are dumped in them.

Bedding – common feature of 'sedimentary' rocks, usually indicating a change in the pattern of sedimentation. Very thin bedding is known as 'lamination' (as frequently found in 'shale').

Calcareous – containing some proportion of 'calcium carbonate'.

Calcite – a crystalline form of 'calcium carbonate'.

Calcium carbonate – an insoluble salt occurring in 'limestone' and other rocks; dissolves in water containing carbon dioxide.

Carbonaceous – as applied to rocks or sediments, contains some carbon from life forms.

Carbonate conclusion – cave, cavity or small hole created by dissolving of calcareous cement and erosion of material.

Carbonate mud – see 'limestone mud'.

Coal – a rock formed from undecayed plant debris which has undergone chemical and physical change. Strictly speaking not a rock (defined as an aggregate of minerals) as it does not contain minerals, but this distinction is best ignored.

Diagenesis – processes affecting sediments at low pressure and low temperature (on or near the earth's surface) and resulting in the formation of a mass of solid rock from loose sediments. See 'lithification'.

Dolerite – 'basaltic' intrusive igneous rock (which did not reach the surface when the molten magma rose up through the crust).

Fault – a crack in bedrock; can be a few centimetres to many kilometres, can be deep or shallow, can be active or passive. Often caused by tectonic activity.

Flaggy sandstones – thinly bedded sandstone which easily splits on bedding.

Fore-reef limestone – 'reef limestone' laid down, often with thin bedding that dips down towards the deeper sea basin. See 'apron reef limestone'.

Fossil – the preserved form of ancient animals or plants or traces left by them. The hard parts are either preserved or replaced by another mineral (such as 'calcite' or quartz). The term is also applied to preserved geological features, for example a fossil sea bed or fossil cliff.

Grit – a 'sedimentary' rock made from large particles of sand. No longer an accepted term for academic purposes but is too well established to be ignored.

High – higher land in a basement or present-day surface.

Knoll reef limestone – a mud-mound reef that is built up above 'shelf limestone' on a 'limestone platform'. Also known as mud-mounds, bio-herms and Waulsortian banks.

Lamination – very thin 'bedding' as occurs in 'shale'. See 'bedding'.

Limestone – a general name for any sedimentary rock containing more than 50 percent calcium carbonate usually, but not always, derived from animal shells and skeletons. There are many different types of limestone and a considerable variety of limestones within the Peak District.

Limestone mud – very fine calcium carbonate particles, secreted by algae and other micro lifeforms, forms a well-cemented limestone; 'limestone reefs' are frequently made of limestone mud.

Limestone platform – a large platform of limestone built up on an area of higher sea floor, bounded by basins. Platforms contain roughly five types of limestone: 'shelf limestone', 'knoll reef limestone', 'apron reef limestone', 'ramp limestone' and 'slope limestone'; together these form 'platform limestone'. 'Basin limestone' is deposited alongside the platform.

Limestone reefs – see 'apron reef limestone' and 'knoll reef limestone'.

Lithification – the process of forming a 'rock' from loose material (such as sand grains) both close to the earth's surface and deeper in the crust (following subsidence, deep burial, etc.).

Lithology – name for the general characteristics such as composition and texture of rocks, usually sedimentary rocks but not always.

Lithosphere – the 'sphere of the rocks', combines the crust and outer mantle to form tectonic plates.

Mantle – the layer of the earth between the crust and the core; divided into the inner mantle and outer mantle with the crust and outer mantle forming the lithosphere or tectonic plates.

Metamorphic – rock formed from another type of rock that has undergone physical, temperature or chemical transformation.

Mineralisation – process where gases and fluids from heated lower layers of the crust pass up through faults and cracks, causing changes to rock and depositing minerals, some of economic value.

Mineral vein – line, usually found along a fault, where mineralisation has taken place.

Mudstone – made from mud grains eroded from land and deposited as sediments in a sea or lake or river, then hardening into rock.

Plate tectonics – see 'tectonic plate'.

Platform limestone – generic name for 'limestones' laid down on the shelf, ramp or slope of a 'limestone platform'.

Rake – see 'mineral vein'.

Ramp limestone – 'limestone' laid down on the ramp of a 'limestone platform'.

Reef limestones – see 'limestone reefs'.

Rock – an aggregate of minerals.

Sandstone – a 'sedimentary' rock made from sand grains eroded from land and deposited as sediments in a sea or lake or river, then hardening into rock.

Sedimentary – rocks formed from sediments dumped in seas, lakes and rivers. Limestone, sandstone, shale, etc. are all sedimentary rocks. Other categories of rock are 'igneous' (volcanic) and 'metamorphic'.

Shale – made from mud grains eroded from land with the addition of a small amount of carbonaceous material, deposited as sediments in a sea or lake or river, then hardening into rock. Shale is usually dark in colour, laminated into thin layers or beds and is soft and friable. No longer an accepted term for academic purposes but is too well established to be …

213

... ignored. (Rreplaced by 'claystone', sometimes with a qualifier such as laminated, sometimes without. The distinction between a mudstone showing no lamination and a shale is lost under this system without the qualifier.)

Shelf limestone – 'limestone' laid down on the main part of a 'limestone platform'.

Siltstone – a 'sedimentary rock' made from silt grains eroded from land and deposited as sediments in a sea or lake or river, then hardening into rock.

Shake hole – see 'sink hole'.

Sink hole – hole in the surface of limestone into which surface water drains. Also known as 'swallow hole', 'swallet', 'shake hole'.

Stromatolite – fossilised form of algae, common in 'reef limestones'.

Swallow hole – see 'sink hole'.

Swallet – see 'sink hole'.

Tectonic activity – earthquakes, folding, faulting and earth movements (up, down and/or lateral) caused by the interaction of 'tectonic plate' boundaries.

Tectonic plate – the earth's surface is divided into a series of interlocking but independent plates of which there are two types: continental and oceanic. Tectonic plates or the 'lithosphere' consist of the earth's outer layer, the crust and the next inner layer, the outer mantle. There is a discontinuity between the outer mantle and the inner mantle and the plates move around on this discontinuity, propelled by convection currents within the inner mantle.

Index of Place Names